People Of The Book

What people are saying about *People of The Book*

"Well conceived, beautifully crafted, and a great read. The window into a Jew's religious life is well worth the price of this novel."

— *D. Robins, Int'l MGA Journal*

"From cover to cover, riveting. Muchnick skillfully, artfully draws the reader into the heart and soul of one Jewish man's experience as he discovers his Mashiach."

— *G. Cottrell*

"The sweet simplicity of this book reveals the sweet simplicity of the gospel of Jesus Christ. This easy flowing novel should be read by Jews and Christians alike."

— *E. Bakow*

"Finally, a Jewish story told with warm tenderness of heart about an orthodox Jew's journey to know his Messiah."

— *M. Molling*

"Most recently read People of The Book. It certainly is well written. I have always been interested in glimpses into the Jewish culture. She needs to keep writing."

— *Dr. Roy Baker, Superintendent of Schools*

"I loved it. I read it over and over. It's brilliant."

— *Myrna Conger, Seattle Temple Matron*

"I've never before looked at the painting like that. And the characterization is excellent. The story line pulled me right into the book, deep into the character. You brought Yesod alive; he thinks and feels as a real person... I could feel his deep love of the Jew praying, and his conflicts. I could identify with Yesod's quest for spiritual truth."

— *Jerry Proudlock, bookstore supervisor, author*

"This book is important to help us understand our Jewish friends' religious lives, as well as being a captivating spiritual story and a romance. When I read this book for the second time, I learned more about the Jewish thoughts, feelings and conversations of the hero in a wonderful way. I better understood his worship, his banter with friends, the romantic hopes of his engagement, and what a Jew thinks about Jesus the Christ."

— *D. Baker*

People Of The Book

Am HaSefer Torah

By

Marlena Tanya Muchnick

Distributed by:

Granite Publishing and Distribution, LLC
868 North 1430 West
Orem, Utah 84057
(801) 229-9023 • Toll Free (800) 574-5779
Fax (801) 229-1924

Page Layout & Design by Myrna Varga • The Office Connection, Inc.
Cover Design by Tammie Ingram

Savior Praying in Gethsemane
by Harry Anderson
©by Intellectual Reserve, Inc.

ISBN: 1-932280-12-X
(previously published by 1st Books ISBN: 1-4033-0584-6)
Library of Congress Control Number: 2003106362
Printed in the United States of America

First Printing, July 24, 2003

10 9 8 7 6 5 4 3 2 1

Acknowledgments

The author wishes to thank David Robins for his inspired insights and faith in my abilities. He has provided indispensable editorial, philological and scholarly assistance with this novelette. My deepest gratitude is to Daniel, my husband. His spirituality and many talents have greatly enriched my life and work.

For Bill, Dori and Pam…
We are family

Other books by this author:

Notes of a Jewish Convert to the LDS Church: Conversion of a Soul

Life Changing Testimonies of the Lord Jesus Christ

Adventures With the Angels of Love

ECHAD

(One)

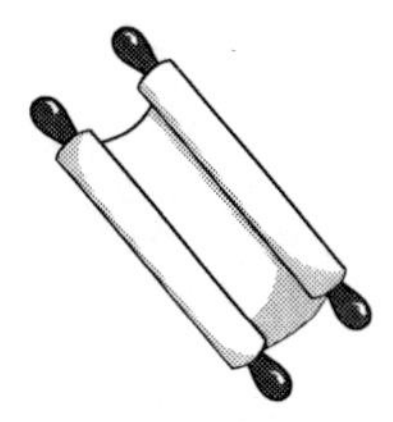

Old things can become new.
New things can become old.
New things can become holy.
—Talmudic saying

Yesod Chai Eleazer pulled his black coat around his spare and hunched frame and hurried toward the synagogue ahead. Gray, drizzling rain fogged his thick glasses, cutting off the world ahead of his eyes. *"Vay is mere,"*[1] he complained to the rain running off the rim of his black hat. "*Meshugah*[2] rain." He moved faster, knowing that in five minutes he would be late for Friday night services, which he never missed. The winter night obliterated any view of a sundown to mark the start of *Shabbat*.[3] He had visions that the nine other men needed for the *minyan*[4] tonight were all hurrying, too. For it was better in the eyes of the Eternal One if,

---

[1] Oh, dear me
[2] Crazy, wild, absurd
[3] Refers to Sabbath, sundown Friday to sundown Saturday
[4] Quorum of 10 Jewish men required to begin a religious service

gathered like one body at the doors of G-d's house, all ten men entered His sanctuary as one to begin the traditional services.

A moment later he saw the familiar brownstone building, Temple *B'nai Israel*, a narrow brown monolithic presence in the gloom. He sighed in relief that only one, Strasser, had arrived. He could tell by the man's huddled apparition. Gelber soon arrived, pacing impatiently in front of the door. Valenkov and Malkhot, two of the best singers, converged from other directions. He saw them greet each other in the rain. Then Gevurah, the attorney, whooshed up to the curb and stepped out of his Cadillac. He was always prompt, Yesod remembered with a cynical grunt.

"G-d's laws are immutable, and His timetables do not allow us much latitude of negotiation," Gevurah would say. He was the very tick of time, never without both his wristwatch and his father's legacy to him, a 24-carat gold pocket watch, carried in his side pocket, against his hip. He also wore a pager on his belt in case important clients discovered the need for his services day or night. Gevurah often fiddled with these several devices so they would work in that perfection of tireless harmony that he expected from all things, human or divine. Now eager to enter the sanctuary, his key pushed into the brass slit of the lock. He deftly turned it and the echo of its click sounded emptily in the maw of blackness that gaped inside the building.

Hesed arrived as Yesod crossed the street to join everyone. "*Shabbat sholom*, a peaceful Sabbath," he said. Already he had his *yarmulke*[5] on his head.

Yesod said, "Three more. Where are Simon and *ben Abuyah*? And what of Kezetsky, is his wife keeping him from *Shabbat*?"

"They will come. They rarely miss. Don't worry, my friend," Hesed reassured. His smile was soft, his eyes filled with mirth and happiness that shone beneath bushy black brows. For much of his thirty years he had cared for his parents, working in their store by day, creating wonderful drawings in his room at night. These he would sell to members of the congregation for holiday gifts. Yesod and he had been classmates and remained good friends.

"To come to the house of G-d this night for worship, it's *vunderlech!*[6] Today, you should believe it, is a day of love. Tonight I began a drawing of this very synagogue."

"*Mazeltov*,"[7] said Yesod, genuinely happy for him. "I'll come to see it when you finish. I'll invite you to hang it in my book-store."

"Precisely four minutes and counting," droned Gevurah looking at his timepieces. "We will wait until five more minutes have passed, no longer. Maybe others will come and take their places, as before."

Six minutes later, they were ten. Laughing with glee they pushed each other inside the blackness, a bearded body of Jews eager to bring themselves before the Eternal One as children

---

[5] Skullcap worn by Jewish men who observe the Law of Moses
[6] Wonderful
[7] Congratulations, good luck

before their approving, beloved parents.

Of the three synagogues in Yesod's city, his was the smallest, the emptiest, and the most beautiful. Built fifty years ago as a Hare Krishna temple, its occupants had relocated to the west of the city several years earlier to attract a younger congregation and a cadre of orange-robed young men eager to become missionaries. Old Rabbi Schechter, looking for a prime location for his Conservative worshippers, visited the site with Cantor Aaron Rosten. They immediately felt a spirit of peace. Standing in the bowels of the sanctuary they looked up at stained glass clerestory windows sixty feet above them and their eyes filled with awe. It was as if they saw instead the symbol of G-d's presence, the *Ner Tamid*,[8] candle of the Eternal Light, securely encased in an iron and glass globe, moving from side to side in a fated dance with gravity just over the imaginary Holy of Holies partition below. They fell in love with the place.

They made an offer but the Hare Krishnas were considering a sale to a chain of meditation centers. Negotiations dragged on several months until finally Rabbi Schechter mortgaged his home and threw a hundred hundred-dollar bills onto the bargaining table. When their offer was accepted, the congregation cleaned and refurbished everything they could reach and opened with pride and fanfare in time to sell tickets to *Yom Kippur*[9] services.

For a while the new congregation, the only Conservative

---

8 "Everlasting Light" in synagogue—commemorates Chanukah
9 Jewish Day of Atonement

synagogue for forty miles, drew many of the curious from the two Reform tabernacles within a commutable radius. Holiday services were well advertised in Yiddish, Hebrew, and English. Members distributed a thousand flyers; they baked delicious refreshments for the *Kiddush,*[10] *Bar Mitzvahs,*[11] *Chanukah*[12] and weddings; they even formed a choir for sacred holiday services that were broadcast on local radio stations. Cantor Rosten was found to have an inspiring tenor voice.

After a year or two the attendance evened out. There were those who thought the many responsibilities of the Orthodox service were suffocating. Others expressed dislike for the liberalized practices of the Reform synagogue. It was an ever-smaller audience that enjoyed the choir's wails of praise as they climbed up the high, narrow walls in trembling vibrato. But the devout only shrugged at their dwindling number, for when that most sacred holiday, *Yom Kippur*, the Day of Atonement, came around, Cantor Rosten's melancholy prayers meandered and twisted in agony across the vault-like room. His pleadings in their behalf hung on the somber scale of his voice until his congregation wept. In a tenor deeply moving and full of rhythmic mourning for the sins of a people, the Cantor called out to G-d to comfort His flock while the rabbi and his small community of worshipers unburdened themselves to the Almighty in passionate prayer.

Yesod Chai Eleazer was always in the throng of the faithful,

---

[10] Prayer ceremony sanctifying Jewish Sabbath

[11] Confirmation ceremony for 13-year-old—rite of passage to manhood

[12] Feast of Dedication celebrating victory over Maccabees. See Glossary.

his own strong voice raised in praise each Friday evening and every Saturday morning and evening. Everyone knew him. No holiday passed without his loyal attendance, no celebration was missed, and few *Bar Mitzvah* boys could say they had taken upon them the solemn duties of a Jewish *mensch*[13] without the strong hand of the spare-framed Yesod pumping theirs in joyous acclamation. Like the perpetual sign in his bookstore window that read Sale in Progress, Yesod Chai Eleazer was a spirited fixture amid changelessness.

Yet, for all his participation, he had a secret passion he pursued more and more. This was the study of a work stemming from the Jewish mystical movement that began in the Middle Ages. Mystics wondering how humankind might spiritually understand the Almighty had written their arcane and complex theories as a serious attempt at what G-d's plan for Jews might be. A pious attempt at fathoming the mysteries of G-d and creation, the *Kabbalah*[14] was a compilation of seldom read speculation on things esoteric that in time became as threads in the fabric of Judaism.

One theory sets forth a possible scenario for the coming of the Jewish *Mashiach,*[15] and largely for this reason Yesod was an avid reader. Portions of the Aramaic *Kabbalah* had taken up residence in his brain. Sometimes when he was in deep concentration upon the *siddur*[16] prayers, a thin ray of light seemed to illuminate in his

---

[13] Gentleman
[14] Body of Jewish mystical and esoteric thought
[15] Messiah
[16] Jewish prayer, guide and songbook for holidays, special observations

mind, and he was brought what he could only say was a message. He felt he was in tune with manifestations of the holy lights and powers of G-d.

Now he concentrated on the emanation of the *Shekinah*, a divine Presence that was said to be the actual Spirit of G-d. For what purpose was the Sabbath if not to welcome in that symbol of perfect holiness that will bring forth from its hiding place in the ether of the universes the longed-for Messianic era, the arrival of the Jewish *Mashiach*?

Yesod had read often of Jews drawn to the belief that Jesus the teacher was really Jesus the Christ. This error in reasoning he attributed to their feelings of deprivation, having a savior who was always promised but never seemed to arrive. To Yesod these people were fools, rebels, *herem*,[17] *galuts*,[18] from the traditions of their ancestors. Rabbi Schechter had told Yesod that the Messiah was no single man, but instead a term that referred to a time of universal brotherhood and redemption. In other words, Messianism was no more than an elaborate metaphor for the banishment by G-d of evil, a time when all mankind would finally experience a peaceful world, a joyous existence. But Yesod was somehow uneasy with his rabbi's explanation. In this way he was different from the others in his congregation.

Sometimes Yesod guardedly shared his understanding of *Kabbalah* with Gevurah and Hesed, and more openly with Sofia

---

[17] Turncoat
[18] Alienation, the exiled

Tiferet, his fiancée, who accepted the ideas gradually. But to the average Jew, the many-layered allusions and symbolisms of the ancient *Kabbalah* writings were indecipherable, and all but the very mystery-minded of Jewish men were suspect of its wisdom, for stories were circulated of rabbis gone mad from too much contemplation of its mysteries.

But to Yesod, the book of *Kabbalah* was like the mysterious hidden sea that moves imperceptibly beneath the blind crust of earth. It beckoned him at this time in his life, and he became a stealthy seeker of that deepest and most arcane wisdom. He wanted passionately to apprehend, to immerse his soul in the cosmic alliance between the Almighty One and every human action. While most Jews in his congregation were content to come to services and enjoy each other's company, Yesod's mind flew not from verse to verse but from concept to concept. It was common for him to read the *Talmud*[19] *Torah*[20] and books on the sages while the rabbi spoke about contributions and meeting times. After synagogue he was usually at the rabbi's door with questions of law or philosophy, and the other members always stood back to let him pass. He was even approached from time to time to perform an occasional *bris*[21] when the cantor and the rabbi were out of town. His mother, Binah, often expressed pride in her learned son, but neither she nor the others detected the restlessness in his soul.

---

[19] Book of rabbinical commentary upon Torah. See Glossary

[20] First five books of Old Testament, in Hebrew, with commentary

[21] Circumcision ceremony (Hebrew: *brit milah*—covenant cut) for male infants at 8 days. Known as the Seal of G-d. Refers to the perpetuation of Israel as promised by G-d in Genesis 17:10, 21:4

SHENEI

(Two)

The service tonight had begun with the usual *Shabbat Sholom*,[22] a song of happiness and joy welcoming in *Shabbat*, led by Rabbi Schechter. Yesod moved his body to the ritualized, meandering tune, repeating *a capella* the Hebrew words in the *minyan* in unison with the others. Yarmulkes of white, black, and embroidered red and gold bobbed up and down emphasizing the words. A few more members had filtered in, two couples who sat together and several boys who had been *Bar Mitzvah*ed the year before. Each worshipper then opened the *siddur* to the section called *Shabbat* and Festival Services, to begin the long service with songs of praise. The book, opened from the right, featured Hebrew on the right page and a fair English translation on the left. The

[22] Sabbath peace

congregation sang the melodies as they had been taught, *a capella* and from memory, for there are no musical notations in a *siddur*.

Yesod closed his eyes and sang in Hebrew the opening Psalm 95 by heart, as he had done most of his thirty-four years. The words he knew. They were engraved on his heart, a conduit from a timeless world to the present, from the robes of prophets to the present day fabrics that layered his skin. Hebrew words unchanged since antiquity rose from the few gathered there and surrounded them like a tapestry of voices living and past. Guttural sounds, ritual mutterings meant only for the Eternal One's ear, they were like a spell cast upon the chorus as well. As in all Jewish liturgy, Yesod sang to celebrate the past because it cemented his faith to G-d in memory of an entire nation scattered like sand but enduring as earth. Cantor Rosten's voice trembled with emotion at his words. His vibrato rumbled throughout the room. The simple, ageless melodies proceeded until six had been sung.

How reassuring this was, yet in his intense concentration Yesod looked pained. His visage appeared characteristically pinched and irritated, as if his soul were on a sacred quest and had despaired permanently of consolation and food, though he ate his meals ravenously. His nose was reminiscent of ancient Abrahamic-Arabic emblems, a protean protrusion between his eyes. The bridge extended in broad forward arch, bent upon forceful extrusion, then sloped smartly downward toward its nares, a tiny boomerang of cartilage, a canopy of flesh, a rounded slice of hill on a narrow ramp of face.

He always appeared preoccupied with difficult thoughts, and

indeed he often was. He'd developed the habit of hunching his back when intense in thought or prayer, reading *Kabbalah* aloud in his room, or shelving volumes onto the crowded pine thoroughfares of his bookstore. At these times, his nostrils would flare and his dark eyes took on a hawk's glare through the lenses of his wire-rims. His mouth alone seemed to smile in its precarious perch beneath his nares, and this gave him a somewhat laughable mien at times. He had not yet begun to bald, but he wore a short beard like many in his synagogue. He looked indefensibly Jewish.

Now Yesod swayed jerkily to the chanting in a little sideways dance, his head keeping to the steady beat. Sometimes he tried to visualize the very first desert wanderers, castoffs, ragtag Hebrews trudging in the wake of prophets, camping along the scorching shores of the Dead Sea or traveling slowly on foot. Families in exile beneath a desert blazing with heat that leathered their skins and cooked thin meal into thinner page-shaped *matzoh*[23] crackers on their backs.

Thoughts of *matzoh* left him hungry for his mother's *Shabbat* meal that he knew awaited.

> *"Acknowledge the Lord, all families of nations; acknowledge His majestic power. Acknowledge his glory and bring Him tribute. Amayn."*[24]

Suddenly a reassuring picture of a familiar form came to him, smiling from another time. "Who are you?" his grandfather

[23] Unleavened bread, usually in cracker form
[24] Amen

Schupak had asked him one nearly forgotten *Shabbat* morning as they walked to breakfast before *schul*.[25] "Who do you say that you are, little *Chaili*?"

"What do you mean, *zayde*?[26] I am Yesod." A child of eight, Yesod took his *zayde*'s hand as they neared an intersection.

"Ah, mine boychik. You are Yesod, yes. You are Chai. That means 'life'. But first you are a Jew, a Jew. You are one of G-d's chosen! Can you remember that, Yesod Chai Eleazer? You are here to remember your people and your past and your tradition, and by the way, your parents and grandparents, too."

He laughed in delight at the boy's worshipful expression. *Zayde*'s beard was a white emblem of age, he was the family patriarch and because his name was Moishe, Moses in English, Yesod knew that his grandfather was that very prophet, who led his people across a tossing ocean to the safety of America's golden promise.

The old man had given Yesod a faded picture of himself, and it sat like a sort of shrine on the boy's dresser in his room at home as he grew to manhood. *Zayde*'s piercing eyes were like a sage's beacon of righteousness to Yesod, who felt that the fire of his grandfather's passionate Jewishness had been passed to him like a mantle.

His mother, Binah, would reminisce about her life in the old country. Yesod always listened hardest when she talked about her

---

[25] Synagogue
[26] Grandfather

father. Morris was then a burly fishmonger from Byelorussia during the late 1800's. Moishe, a *Hasid*[27] and a reader of the mystical *Kabbalah*, married a comely Polish widow eleven years his senior with a disappointingly small dowry, for the Jews of that area were not allowed to prosper. But Anna Janowska helped him in his business until she proudly bore him their one daughter, Binah, whom she named after the table in the synagogue upon which the *Torah* is read. Binah became a devoutly religious girl with a strong mind that attracted several well-situated suitors. In the spring of 1917 she chanced to meet and fall in love with a lonely magistrate. He lost no time in asking Moishe for Binah's hand in marriage. But before the ceremony could take place, war that had only been growling rumors broke out in Russia reaching treacherous tentacles into the *Pale*'s[28] *schtetls*[29] where the *Hasidic Ashkenazim*[30] were confined.

Moishe was in the field when they came to his home. He and Anna hid, and from a gully they watched their home burned. Binah and Keter, now her betrothed, joined them, and the little group fled by night through the broad cold valley to the coast of the Black Sea where in time, they managed to join an underground movement with roots in Germany. They married there and, with the grandparents, emigrated to America on the tail of the war. Binah felt her safety assured. Soon she discovered new resolve and

---

[27] A pious Jew
[28] Area between Baltic and Black Sea where Jews were banished for some 600 years
[29] Jewish communities in eastern Europe during WWII
[30] Name applied to Jews of Central and Eastern Europe

purpose as an Americanized Jew. Fervently she prayed to the Almighty for a son of the Covenant in this free land that she might contribute her own purse of life to the wealth of a prospering nation.

Now the Sabbath night congregation stood and in loud and joyous voice sang the traditional *L'Kha Dodi*, the welcoming in of the Sabbath bride. Yesod proudly repeated the evocative words of commitment and praise to his beloved G-d. The words came not from the living, it seemed, but from ancient lives, and the voices around him rose and fell in happy unison, like the undulating hills of verdant Jerusalem.

L'kha dodi likrat kallah, p'nei Shabbat n'kab'lah. Come, my beloved, with chorus of praise, Welcome *Shabbat* the Bride, queen of our days.

They were coming to the part where the *Shabbat* bride is greeted. Yesod felt the sweet pain of hot tears touch the edges of his eyes. *Come in peace, soul mate, sweet gift of the Lord, greeted with joy and in song so adored.* He faced the marbled *Torah* ark, inscribed with a magnificent crown reminiscent of Babylonian splendors beneath the flickering glow of the Eternal Light, then turned to the left and to the right, following the rabbi.

Amidst G-d's people, in faith in accord. Come, Bride Shabbat; come, crown of the days. Peace, come into my heart, Yesod prayed.

He felt a calm joy in this room. It was a canopy of assurance that his G-d was like no other, infinitely unknowable yet available and eager to bless His chosen people in their travails upon the

earth where, in His wisdom, He had placed them.

Then, as Yesod opened his eyes to the continuous flicker of the *Ner Tamid* before him a filmy white haze seemed to come from the ceiling and settle over the congregation. He wondered quickly if anyone else could see it. He blinked and rubbed his eyes. But there it was, swaying to an imperceptible wind, hovering, a benign presence.

Ah, yes, he thought. *There you are again*.

Since his foray into *Kabbalah* study a year earlier, this mystical event was not new to him. It was as if he were being summoned. In a moment more Yesod felt a sweet peacefulness, and was transported above the others. Their voices seemed to fade and he thought he caught a distant strain of music. Yes, he was sure of it. Everyone else's attention was centered on their *siddur*.

The strange manifestation lasted only a few moments then faded. The white haze vanished, still Yesod felt unusually uplifted by the visit, and he hoped the feeling would stay with him. The room resumed its usual yellow glare from the *Shabbat* lights. He wondered if anyone else had been affected, then decided they hadn't. It was a sign, he believed, a test of spiritual sensitivity.

"G-d's power is greater than our own," Rabbi Schechter was saying. "He created all things and made all things subject unto Him. Every *Shabbat* we celebrate the Almighty One's power to recreate the world and in our thankfulness and prayers we find new life."

Chai. The secret of survival. *Amayn.* The promise to the Jew,

and of course, to all others. *Amayn*.

The congregation turned to symbolically greet the bride of the Sabbath.

Again Yesod's fertile imagination took over. Instead of seeing a formless "bride of Sabbath" enter the room he saw before him Sofia Tiferet, his *shayna*,[31] his betrothed. Framed within the narrow hall light pouring in the doorway, he willed her to take shape before him. Her black eyes, that carbonite gift of her dark *Sephardim*[32] heritage, gazed upon him. Immediately he felt a rush of love and desire that came without warning. He saw then her olive skin, her radiant, serene countenance, her high and prominent cheekbones, a mark of strength so reminiscent of her Spanish-Turkish ancestors. She moved toward him quickly, her image melding with his. Her full mouth reached his own in that moment and he became excited by her imagined touch, almost as he'd been on that night of nights three months earlier when she agreed to become his wife. Sofia Tiferet, his beautiful beloved, for whom he had waited all his life as a man. He embraced her in daylight's work and again in the flowing darkness of his dreams.

He knew that at morning's Sabbath service they would sit together but not yet as one. He would lose himself in her perfume. Yesod ached with longing to know the secret of this woman, so mystical in her beauty. Her dark eyes were to him an inviting pathway to the most intimate fulfillment. With his arm around her

---

[31] Beautiful in character, spirit

[32] From Sepharad, referring to Spain, Spanish, Moroccan and Portuguese Jews

he would feel her warmth, he would touch her thigh with his as they stood together listening to the *Torah* scroll being read.

Thinking on this, a sigh of love tore from his stomach. Soon, but not soon enough, their wait would end. The bridal *huppah*[33] he would help to build and she to decorate, would be a celebration of their bonding hearts. Why could he not seize it all now?

Rabbi Schechter had begun the *Ma'ariv* service in which the *Sheckinah*, G-d's presence, is freed from all evil forces to seek union with the holy light of the Almighty, that all judgements one of another may cease and blessings of peace might flow freely throughout the world. Yesod looked over at Gevurah who always sang this section loudly, stroking his gray beard and raising his hand with the music, as if to add his separate blessings on unseen heads. Hesed looked at him in amusement and then at Yesod and winked. Yesod knew Hesed was waiting for the service to end so they could *kibbitz*[34] over the *Kiddush* wine and treats. Often they set out for Yesod's home for an hour or two of intense, scholarly discussion, which invariably led to an argument over Yesod's favorite subject, the coming of the Jewish *Mashiach*. Afterward, he would bid his mother a good night and in the quiet of his room begin an hour of study about the *Sheckinah*, his favorite subject, the ponderous, mysterious, nearly magical presence of G-d. At these times, he often felt like the small child he once had been,

---

[33] Canopy over couple during marriage
[34] Talk, josh, tease, flatter

protected and nurtured within the confines of his parent's home, reading before bedtime.

Yesod and his family lived in a three bedroom house two miles west of the business district. Close to his store, it afforded him the family unit as well as the preservation of capital for when he married. It was a warm place, musty with time, but pleasant, filled with inherited couches, pillows, and breakfronts that held several sets of Sabbath and Passover dishes, lined up like icons of a once orthodox Jewishness. These were used with no regularity except the yearly feasts of Passover, *Yom Kippur,* and *Rosh HaShonah*.

Keter, Yesod's father, could not trace his ancestry past paternal grandparents and didn't see why he should sit all day reading *Torah* when his Jewry was uncertain and there was work to be done in the world. He became a plumber. This left Binah to keep *kosher*[35] or not, however she fancied, and to raise her only son. She was an efficient and purposeful woman with a penchant for politics, anxious to partake of what America could offer her, so she enrolled in night school and helped to support her family as a teacher-nanny to the children of rich German Jews. This somewhat aggravating employment seemed to heighten awareness of her Polish-Russian heritage.

Every Sabbath morning, Binah defiantly *schlepp*ed[36] Yesod to the neighborhood synagogue, *B'nai Israel.* He loved the smell of mahogany and candle wax. He attended Hebrew school, learning

---

[35] In accord with Old Testament dietary laws
[36] Carry, drag along

quickly, and so was often invited to read with the rabbi. Binah saw to it that he was *Bar Mitzvah*ed and that he stayed pure. She found him a profitable business nearby in used books and taught him to keep clean records. He was a good boy and obedient, but just to be sure, Binah told him never to touch a woman before they stood under the marriage *huppah*.

"Make more of yourself, *Chaili*. Open many businesses, there is much to achieve in America. Marry well and make your parents proud and your grandparents and all our family in Russia and Poland. Remember, you are a Jew. This is your duty." Then, deciding the essential issues had been addressed, Binah turned her attention to women's organizations and local politics and left Yesod to the Almighty's watchful eyes.

The *Shabbat* service would soon be completed. Yesod, pulling his thoughts from Sofia, covered his eyes with the congregation to sing the *Shema*.[37] The small gathering faced the *Torah* ark once again and *davened*[38] before it in quick bows. Now they would recite the *Shema*. Yesod likened this to worshipping at the throne of the Eternal One, it echoed in his heart as a single divine edict, the defining marker that forever sets Jews apart from their brethren, the Creedal prayer.

Shema, Yisroel, adonai elohenu, adonai echod. Hear, O Israel, the Lord our G-d, the Lord is One.

The *Shema* was a point of hope, a white flame of truth that

---

[37] Jewish creedal prayer
[38] Bending forward and back from knees while praying

tamed the whirlwind of days and nights with one unchangeable truth. In this Yesod believed with all his might. Jews were the *chosen people* because they had sought G-d's deliverance, and they alone had promised Him unfailing and eternal allegiance. Yesod believed himself an extension of that promise. How could there be even the whiff of another G-d? Yesod's mind was suddenly pierced by a thought: When the *Mashiach* would come, how would it be, the announcement, the entrance? Would he assume the Almighty's earthly shadow? How would men regard him? *How will I know him*? These thoughts he had entertained secretly for years, with no progress toward an answer.

Lately, because of his *Kabbalah* readings, his attention had focused on these things repeatedly. Often in his store between customers, and in the solitude of his room at night, he opened the book and read. Tonight the subject was purity of the soul. Highest of G-d's creations, a human soul becomes obligated to descend to mortality, becoming in the process unattached from G-d, "from a high mountain to a deep pit" the *Talmud* states. Now the soul must fight to conform to G-d's higher laws from a lesser vantage point, with fervent hope of returning to Him on a higher plane after death. The long-awaited *Mashiach* will be an integral part of this resurrection. These ideas Yesod had discussed with Rabbi Schechter on numerous occasions, but the Rabbi told Yesod to concentrate on being useful and charitable "in the now," "for we can do nothing about the mysterious and distant future."

The service, nearing close, embraced the *Aleinu*, a traditional prayer of praise. This was followed by the *Yigdal* hymn, based

upon the thirteen principles of faith left to mankind by the great rabbi and prophet, Moses Maimonides. Yesod recited these in Hebrew, looking at his friend Gevurah still absorbed in studious contemplation. Hesed, standing at Yesod's extreme left met his glance, and together they watched each other mouth the imperishable words of truth. Repetition cast its spell upon them all.

There is a Creator who alone made all things. One, unique, he is eternal but has no form. He alone is worshipped. The prophets are true, and Moses was a prophet. Our Torah is divine, immutable. G-d knows all of us, and He rewards and punishes us for our thoughts and deeds. The Mashiach will come. He will resurrect the dead.

Finally the service ended. Everyone shook hands and beamed. Hesed was the first one at the *Kiddush* table laden with *kosher* wine and the white chocolate-iced cakes his wife had given him to bring. He loved to eat rich foods when he could get them. His thin wife kept her jolly husband on a perpetual diet. He was also too generous with the Mogen David grape, but tonight there was more than enough for all. Rabbi Schechter offered the *Kiddush* prayer and everyone ate hungrily.

"*Shabbat shalom, Shabbat shalom*," Hesed wished everyone well as he poured each person a small cupful. "Yesod, your place or mine this week?"

Yesod joined his friend at the refreshment table, grabbing a large slice of cake.

"My house, tonight. My mother will give us to eat. I smelled a chicken cooking when I passed the kitchen!"

"Your house, then. I'll tell Gevurah. Let us toast to a new week, a prosperous week for all and may you sell many books."

"And may the dead increase at your door," Yesod joked. Hesed Shapolsky's Memorial Headstone Company was around the corner from Yesod's bookstore.

Hesed countered that some of Yesod's books had been on his shelves so long they could be used as headstones, saving everyone a bundle of *gelt*[39] and providing them with a "novel" way to pass the time while they visited their departed.

So, after *Kiddush* they headed to Yesod's, happy that the rain had stopped and the sky had cleared of its confusion so numbers of stars could be seen above the trees.

[39] Cash

SHALOSH

(Three)

The next day was Sunday, and Yesod was at work unloading a box of books that Miriam Weiner had brought in that morning. It contained a set of heavy, once popular and imposing encyclopedias that Mrs. Weiner had long ago purchased new. Her children had grown and moved away. You never could tell, she reasoned. Maybe her David or her Rachel would read the volumes and see in them a glorious future and make her so proud it would carry her through the monotony of her own life.

Yesod frowned. These rescued treasures smelled not of success but of dust, dampness, and disregard. They bred mold. Their condition was advanced, maybe even terminal. The appearance of the pages was abominable, they were even yellowing! Most of the books looked untouched, unread, yet they hadn't spanned a generation! Spines once sturdy were softened. They had been

carelessly thrown or made to lean loosely upon each other, until their weight crippled them and they curved inward. They were like a favorite place that had grown wasted with weeds, leaving a stench of slow decay. How did Mrs. Weiner expect him to sell these books, did she think he could work miracles and make them perfect again?

He sighed and marked in pencil a reduced price on the frontspiece of each volume. Then he put a thin paper banner across them that read Seven Volumes—One Low Price, and with a deep sigh, put them on the shelf with all the other forgotten compilations of facts and commentaries that had taken years of unnamed men's lives to record.

Other shelves of Yesod's bookstore did a more lively business. The Special Bargain rack always moved fast. Once in the store it was immediately to the right. Tempting baskets of packaged bagels, rolls, cream cheese, and butter squares on ice attracted readers and browsers to the main stacks that took up the remaining fifteen hundred feet of space. On the outside of each row Yesod had put large printed banners like sails on a mast, each announcing its category in large serif letters. The fiction stacks were located to the right of the entrance behind the bargain table. Here were popular collections and mysteries, first editions, authors by category, by country and some even by rare Jewish writers, European giants of literature, Russian dissidents, Holocaust fiction, and on.

His Arab competitor, a mile away to the east with a store twice the size, once gladly traded Yesod his personal, oversized hand-made red and brown rug for a gold-lettered Arabic edition of the *Qu'ran*, the bible of the Muslims. This rug was the only obvious color spot in the shop.

In the non-fiction section that took up the left side of the main aisle there was art and art history, architecture, anthropology, banking, biology, Buddhism, cooking, carpentry, and on to Judaism, including Yiddish and Hebrew books, *Kabbalah*, and Mosaic law, seventeenth through twentieth century literature of the world, with lots of Russian writers, marketing, macrobiotics, mysticism, poetry from Asher to Tao, then on to zoology, Zoroastrianism and Zen.

There were no books on Christianity or on Jesus Christ. Yesod stoically refused to take them. He also turned away customers who wanted to give him modern bibles because they included the New Testament, which pious Jews must not read (though secretly he had often wondered what it held).

"It's my store, my choice," he told frustrated customers. "Go see Ali a mile east and he will sell you Islam and Christianity. I am Jewish, a student of *Torah*."

Readers could relax at one of several old round tables and chairs in the center of the stacks atop the centralized Arabic rug, complete with good lighting, spare pencils and paper for taking notes or figuring prices. There were cards for all occasions in racks against the walls. The lone checkout stand loomed like a sentinel next to the bagel baskets.

Other than with the occasional help of Sofia, Yesod ran the

store alone. He made a fair living in used books by keeping his overhead very low. Binah reminded him worriedly that his savings were small and warned that he would have to move when he married. This worried Yesod whenever he thought of Sofia's expensive tastes but he would shrug and trust there would always be enough to see them through.

Behind a wall about mid-store a little one-room office and kitchen with a foldout daybed was cleverly hidden. This arrangement allowed Yesod to keep an eye on the customers and their ominous coats with deep pockets, purses, and bags when he stole away for a cup of Lipton tea that he brewed on a hot plate.

Sometimes when Sofia came to help him stock the books and reorder the bagels they would disappear into their "pre-*huppah*" to hold each other. Hidden there from prying eyes and gossiping lips they could argue over finances, negotiate their future, drink tea with lemon and honey, and sigh like old marrieds over their sweet fate. They had known each other only one year, yet they believed in the joining of their destinies.

Sofia was close to her mother, who saw that her sweet, devoted daughter was drawn mightily to Yesod, to his scholarly obsessions and, even more, that she shared his love for Judaism. She worried that the young and lovely child she observed felt possessed by Yesod's passion for her, how impressed she was at how he invariably deferred to her smallest wish, trying always to please her, to win her smile with every phrase Often she heard them speak of the children they planned to have as if they already existed.

"They have your beauty, my *shayna*, my adored," Yesod would say to Sofia in a soft voice, like prophecy. "Now here is the little girl, with a laugh and smile that shames the sun, and a serenity like her mother. And the boy, *kineahora*,[40] he will be a scholar, I will teach him *Torah* and he will prosper in this new age like none before him." Yesod would read to her from the Song of Songs, and Sofia sang him love songs in Ladino, the native language of the *Sephardim*. She let him stroke her hair and sit very near, but when she sensed desire in him she invariably knew to move away, lest they would both forget themselves.

Sofia's sultry beauty brought return customers to Yesod's bookstore, though he hated his awareness of that. He wanted her for himself alone. Sometimes, Yesod had nightmares. He was old and wrinkled and impotent, they had been married so many years. Sofia would come in from shopping, still young and perfect at 70, her face unmarred, her waist still slender after childbirth. She would see him and, repelled, she would run away in horror. This disturbing dream occurred whenever he felt he'd displeased her in some way. He didn't know why she had chosen him to love. He would never be rich like her father. He could offer her only his total fidelity, a promise that his every thought centered upon her contentment and happiness.

"What else can I desire of a husband, Chai Eleazer," she would tease him when he came to her humbled by his deficiencies, and trace his lips with the gentlest touch of a painted finger nail. "To

---

[40] A magic phrase supposed to ward off evil

be in your arms, safe beyond life like the most precious jewel, beloved as Israel in the arms of the Almighty One. What greater comfort can a *Yiddishe madele*[41] know? You will one day be rich and we will raise many perfect children."

Her words gave him ecstasy. He was the luckiest Jew alive! Even his mother told him that as she envisioned her grandchildren.

Yesod would occasionally share his joy with her. "An ugly *Ashkenaz* with a gorgeous *Sephardic* wife," he would laugh and shake his head. "A celestial gift. *Im yhirtze ha-shem, mama-le*: *only if G-d allows it*."

"You will need two jobs to support her, you know." Binah would say. "She is used to living well. Maybe you should go into partnership with her father." But Yesod bridled at this suggestion, though he knew his mother was only concerned for his future.

Yesod thought alternately of his lack of money and Mrs. Weiner's encyclopedia set when Sofia walked quietly into his store, bundled in the expensive coat her father had given her for a birthday present. Yesod thought sardonically that it must cost more than the new gold band he'd given her, but shrugged. He would never let money separate them. Today she smelled faintly of cardamom, a favorite spice of Spanish households. They greeted each other joyfully and she seated herself at his desk.

"Have you had a good day, my darling? How wonderful it would be to have lunch with my husband-to-be."

---

[41] Young Jewish girl

"It's better now that you're here." He told her of Mrs. Weiner's encyclopedia and showed her the wounded spines, which she gently touched, as if by her caress they would be made whole. She looked at him and her lovely face glowed with expectation. He took her soft hands in his, musing that her arms were like branches extending from the seat of her motherhood. They would bring forth children like leaves of an eternal tree. He kissed her young neck and in her warmth he felt he'd found the gateway to her secret pleasures. *Sofia Tiferet, my beloved,* G-d's *gift to me from the earth.*

"One day, Chai Eleazer, you will own this entire block! You will have thousands of new books to sell, a larger store to preside over and many to carry out your wishes on the spot."

Yesod sat beside her. He knew what was coming, but he remained calm.

"And how is this miracle going to come about?" he asked. "I have no money to expand like that. Do you know, Sofia, my *shayna*, the cost of land in this district?" This was becoming a regular discussion. She wanted him to do business like the chain stores, while he opposed the idea.

"Chai, who told you it takes a miracle? You'll have help, you'll see." Her smile was warm and he almost felt his guard drop. But when he remembered that she wanted him to accept her father's money, his defenses remained firm.

"Sofia, I'm a simple man, I don't know from new books, from assistants, from payroll. I know only to trade in used books, this

is the way I run a business, it's uncomplicated, I have time to bargain with the customers, to read, to study *Torah*. Maybe I can get another job somewhere, something will come available."

"Yes, my darling Chai, you are so wise and diligent. I can see you, the owner of a bigger store, two floors, three, old ***and*** new books, and yourself like a scholarly *rebbe*,[42] guiding us to your treasures! All you need, Chai, my *tsetsele*,[43] is someone to help you get there."

She reached out and he came into her arms, smelling the cardamom in her lustrous hair. He was so very susceptible to her urgings, he knew she took strength from her power over him, but her concerns about money made him uneasy. When they married, his father-in-law had offered (at his daughter's private request) to invest in Yesod's business, to bring him up to the level of respectability at which he believed his daughter and grandchildren should be kept. In truth, Yesod appreciated her interest in his business, but he feared the loss of independence he knew would surely follow.

He flinched thinking of the thousands of ill-written, mainly forgettable publisher's discount books he'd receive that would infest his stately shelves like a virus. These would be followed by crowds of people hustling through his quaint narrow doorways demanding new publications, hurrying through the stacks and

---

[42] Teacher or master of Judaism. Variation of rabbi. Rabbis are ordained and paid for their services

[43] Term of endearment

upsetting his carefully organized shelves in their haste. Wholesalers, buyers, and agents would visit him, authors wanting books signings, Sofia's father wanting profit reports. He'd have to hire strangers to make lists and keep tallies and stock his shelves. No, even the *thought* of counting piles of receipts, balancing books, reporting his daily profits to a measuring, calculating father-in-law (the prosperous trader) was too much. He would have no peace.

In truth, Yesod could never be a successful businessman like Sofia's father, who had amassed a visible fortune in antiques. But he was in all other ways a *mensch*. His shoes were inexpensive but always carefully polished, his suits, sometimes from a second hand rack, were regularly pressed and fit him well. True, he lived in his mother's house much like an ordinary tenant, but he took his meals at one end of the large dining room table, the traditional place of respect in Jewish homes. He studied *Torah*, he was a valued member of his synagogue, and he paid his dues promptly when billed.

But when he was sure of being alone and undisturbed by his parents and friends, Yesod pored over *Kabbalah* and dreamed of the day when the long-awaited time of the *Mashiach* would come. Never did he think of schemes in which he could gain riches. He did not aspire to them, but dreamed instead of finding wealth by uncovering the mysteries of G-d.

These things he had never told Sofia, and he did not know why. Maybe she would laugh at him, see him as immature. She understood his love of books and, to a degree, shared it. But no one could understand the importance this piece of territory had

for him. It was not just a place to labor. How could another be made to see his scarred wooden shelves as altars for genius, as hungry mouths to be fed the minds and hearts of a world's literature? Who would treasure his collection of outcasts and dreamers?

Not even Sofia could know his bookstore for the harbor it was to him, a resting place for all the forgotten poetry of the soul, a safe house of mystery, and lore, and wondrous imaginations, salvaged gifts from the Eternal One, works of fascination, of beauty, of eternal truth. No, this was not a business proposition they were discussing. It was an intrusion into the most private corners of his limited life. He felt violated, but he could not express this to her.

He sat down and put his head in his hands.

"Chai, what if we have many children?"

Yesod did not move or speak. He suddenly wished she were not there.

Sofia, sensing she had gone too far, rose, laughed gently at the man before her and came to him. They had had this discussion more than a few times since their engagement, with no resolution. He knew she was right, he couldn't argue with her. He could hear his mother's voice echoing Sofia's words. He had limited savings and the store he leased was becoming more costly every year. It was hard for Yesod to admit publicly, but he was not financially prepared to marry anyone, even at his age. Many times he had prayed for a solution. Now the wedding was only three months away and they were no closer to resolving the problem.

Sofia looked away for a time, her face solemn and peaceful like a painting Yesod had once seen in a gallery a Spanish woman of high birth gazing at her child. Then she gave her betrothed a penetrating glance and smiled in a way that belied her worry. She knelt beside him and took him in her arms. He kissed her cheek and smiled a little.

"Come, my worried love, treat your Sofia Tiferet to a corned beef at the deli, yes?"

So they went to lunch.

ARBA
(Four)

Ali's Good News Bookstore was an icon of Arab culture in a district mainly Chinese. Ali was an old man, heavy set, with the features of his tribe. He kept his beard carefully trimmed and he rubbed a lotion smelling of Arabic spices on his hands. Over the twenty-odd years Ali had been in America he had become somewhat stooped from looking for dropped change on the sidewalks around his store and up the avenue. The pennies, quarters, and half dollars he quietly collected were to Ali a pedestrian's gold and proved there was potential in American capitalism, which he embraced. He kept the coins stored in huge glass jars behind his counter, more as a curiosity than anything else. But Ali occasionally gave alms from these jars to the indigents who wandered in.

"One of the Pillars of Islam, to give to the less fortunate, *Al-*

Zakat. I have even given alms to a Jew!" he said, laughing aloud when he saw Yesod's grimace.

Ali Imran Ismael was a new and used bookseller as well as a collector of many things; pictures and artifacts, rare books on Islam, Jerusalem and Greece. He searched out tomes on early Christianity, including selected editions of the Bible in ancient languages, some with intricate colored plates protected by sheets of tissue that had grown opaque with age, lending to their authenticity and value. Several years earlier, Ali had begun to collect framed pictures of sad Catholic saints and faded Christian scenes. He found there was a good market in these icons. Busts and friezes, copies of Michelangelo paired with other seventeenth century sculptors, lived out their timeless destinies on Ali's storefront windows.

Yesod knew and somewhat envied that Ali had grown rich from discerning where money was to be made in his business and shrewdly putting himself in its path. Greeks, Arabs, Muslims, some Chinese, and canny tourists bargained there, shopping amid the incense rising like dreams of Kubla Khan from small brass bowls placed around the store. Yesod had once visited with Ali and his Persian friends. They drank oily Arabic coffees and Greek *ouzou* wine as they sat together atop several large Persian rugs. They told Yesod they imagined themselves in Saudi. They listened wistfully to the queer high voice of Marisah Muhamed chant songs in a language older than many civilizations. Sometimes after coffee, Ali and his friends would turn toward *Makkah*, the Holy

City, and intone in unison a requisite daily prayer, one of the Five Pillars of Islam.

Among the shoppers at his store, the Jew, Yesod Chai Eleazer, came on an infrequent basis, to *kibbitz* a *bissel*[44] and transact bargains for used books. This was his eleventh year of trading with the Arab. Today he wandered in with six books that had been left in a box at his door. Ali was sweeping the floor.

"*Shalom*. Thanks for sweeping the way clear for me," Yesod said.

"It's not for you, but for the crowds I'm expecting. *Mas salaam* to you, too."

"I come ahead of the crowds today. They're at my store now, but I told them if they have any money left over they should come here."

"I appreciate that, Yesod. Allah will reward you for your good deed." Ali barely smiled behind his broom as he continued sweeping. "The crowds I am speaking of will never imagine a need for your old books. What did you bring me today, more cast-off trash?"

Yesod sighed and settled in a chair near the desk. This was the manner in which they spoke with each other. He took off his hat and overcoat. Above him was the flag of Saudi Arabia, proudly flying off the top of a bookcase, grass-green with exaggerated Arabic script standing out starkly in white across it's skirt,

44 Talk a little bit

underscored by a white scimitar that made him shudder to think of rolling heads. Ali liked to tease Yesod that this store was a mini-Saudi and under Palestinian rule.

"You may visit from your West Bank, but never forget that this is Arab territory. Israel must retreat from their occupation in our lives."

To this comment Yesod would often become fervently Zionist, insisting that Jews were given the covenant to occupy Israel as its only tenant. Over the years many heated discussions took place beneath Ali's flag, but eventually the men would come to a civilized agreement on the main points of law and the belief that negotiation was preferable to conflict. But Yesod did not feel feisty today. Sofia's lofty plans for their future caused him much worry and deliberation. Quietly he put the books, historical commentaries on early Near Eastern culture, in a row before him.

Ali put his broom away and came over. "Who gave you these?" He picked up a book and looked it over, then studied Yesod with his heavy-lidded eyes.

"Someone who knew you'd want them. They were left at my door to deliver. Maybe you have for me something interesting?"

Ali put the book down and poured himself a cup of thick black coffee Yesod wouldn't touch it then pulled out two fig tarts from a bag nearby. Yesod took one of these.

"I might have something, let me show you." He walked around the table and disappeared into the room he had built onto the back of his store. From a portable boom box a woman sang

in Arabic of love and country in tuneless falsetto. Ali emerged with a Saran-wrapped volume and set it before Yesod with flourish.

"Here, this should please you, Yesod. A rare find, from an estate sale. Go ahead, unwrap it and look inside."

Yesod picked up the book. Through the shiny cellophane he could make out the words "New Testament" in faded gold script, the words etched into the parchment of the cover, which was inlaid with gold and silver inscriptions of the Greek key design. He unwrapped it carefully. The inside pages were very thin, in delicate shape, mute victims of the air and dust of atmosphere and time.

"A beautiful book, Ali, but you know I don't sell New Testaments." But he held it in his hands, feeling its weight, trying not to be curious.

"Nor do you sell the *Qu'ran*, but in both there is much knowledge that is important. The history conflicts. Sometimes I study the New Testament with my *Qu'ran*. Have you never read this book?"

They had spoken of this before. Yesod took the position that G-d gave the people of Israel the *Torah* to read as their Law, as well as the holy writings of the rabbinic sages whose testimonies filled the *Talmud*'s pages. True, the *Mashiach* was expected, but of what use to Jews were stories of a false messiah? Still, he was curious and to cover this he began a litany of excuses.

"No, never have I opened it. I have discussed this with you, Ali. A Jew does not read about Jesus Christ. He studies the prophets, the *Talmudic* scholars, and he studies also his *siddur*,

which contains our prayers and songs. We embrace the moment, the day. What good will it do to live as a monk, to renounce the world? Has Jesus brought peace to the world? When has there ever been peace and unity in Israel? What of the Holocaust? How many of my family did I lose in Germany, in Poland, in Russia? Did you ask your Messiah to explain this to you? What good is your New Testament to me? Will it help me run my store, will it show me how to make enough money to support Sofia Tiferet and the children she is planning?"

Against this onslaught of questions Ali put up his hands. A jewel caught the light and gleamed from his ringed fingers. He walked around the corner and picked up his *Qu'ran*.

"Ah, Yesod, you are indeed hard-necked, as it is written. What of your Moses who led your people from Israel? Do you doubt that dead prophets can give living testimony? We of the Muslim faith are simple followers of Allah. I read about this prophet and healer called Jesus. He preached peace, but more, he preached love. It was through Allah's power that this man raised the dead and made whole the lepers. The holy *Qu'ran* says this poor beggar was Allah's helper, a messiah to his people, but not an immortal man, nevertheless. You should read of him because he came to deliver Allah's message of love. Love, Yesod, love is what he taught."

"He taught what many others have taught. True, he healed lepers. There are claims that he raised the dead. But did he help us escape our Roman oppressors? Did he bring an army to rescue the Jewish captives? Did he bring us G-d's light back into this world? No, he was set upon, poor, not even did he have a horse, much less an army. He couldn't even save *himself. How could he be a Messiah?* I take pity on him, I'll say that much." Still he held the book, feeling curiosity creep through his fingers.

There was quiet in the room. They ate their pastries. Ali slurped his oily Arabic coffee. Finally he emptied his cup and belched in satisfaction.

"This Jesus was Mary's son a good man, but very unfortunate. He was not a holy man as we see it, but a strong teacher of righteousness. He tried to lead the wrongdoers to Allah, to whom there is no second. For that I am grateful. You should study him, Yesod. It will bring you peace." With that he turned and disappeared through the back door into his storeroom.

Yesod heard the toilet flush. He knew Ali was religious, but talk of things he did not know left him uncomfortable and defensive. He remembered Isaiah's words about the "leopard lying down with the kid," and chuckled to himself. Vaguely he wondered what Isaiah would have to say about the man Jesus Christ. His fingers began to open the book, but when he heard Ali return he put it down.

"I do have a book for you," Ali said. "Came in last Thursday. It's over there, near those framed pictures, the last shelf, beneath 'Jerusalem'. You'll see it—a thick book all about the 'beautiful' Dead Sea. It has photographs. You'll like it."

"The Dead Sea you give me? That's all I need. Where is the book?"

Yesod walked past the shelves toward the front of the store. There near the window he found a huge red-jacketed volume. He reached for it and browsed among the pictures stacked by the wall. They were junk, he thought, old faded prints of Arabic kings, Byzantine designs, nameless Catholic saints looking horrified at some unseen terror, a man praying beside a tree.

This last picture caught his attention. It was larger than the rest, a good print maybe 24x36. There was only one figure, a man kneeling beside a thick, wide tree trunk. Yesod guessed it was an olive. A sheaf of white light began at the top of the painting and fell liberally across the man's upraised face and shoulders. The branches and leaves made a safe bower above the man's head. The painting's background was somber gray, giving the appearance of morning mist. Yesod felt sudden compassion for the praying man, as though the artist had happened upon a stranger during an intensely private moment.

He studied it further. It could have been a photograph. Its subject's fervent expression made him wonder whether *he* looked like that when he prayed in his room or on High Holy Days. The painting was disturbing because of its simple power. Yesod stood as if rooted there for several minutes, not wanting to move, but he did not know why. He felt a new quietude come over him, almost happiness. *Some Jew on his knees*, Yesod thought, feeling like he'd just happened upon something of great value. Who would paint a picture like that? He wondered how old it was, he'd never seen it in all the years of coming to visit. *Just like Ali to take in junk*. Someone would buy it to cover a hole in a wall. Yesod wondered uneasily why it moved him so. He laughed out loud and turned quickly away.

"I found the book," he called out to Ali. "It was hard to see through the clouds of incense."

"Incense sells books and statuary. You should try it."

Yesod put on his hat and coat. "Maybe I'll serve Mogen David. Better wine than incense." He looked at the New Testament book.

"Serve it free, then, as almsgiving. It isn't fit to drink. *Mas salemma*, Yesod, good night." Ali again picked up the broom to sweep the rug.

Yesod hid a smile. "*Shalom* to you, reader of the *Qu'ran* and the New Testament." He turned to leave for home. Impulsively, he looked back at the picture but it faced away from him, out the window. He could only make out the frame's edge. Then he remembered that his mother would have dinner early for him this evening and he hurried out.

Once on the wet streets he turned west. His car was nearby. Already Yesod was contemplating a bowl of hot green pea soup and buttered bagels. Binah, still the homemaker for her husband and son, had been appointed a city official of some responsibility. Many of her meetings were in the evening, giving Yesod hours to spend with his books after cleaning the dinner dishes and recounting the day's activities with his father.

As he passed an alleyway an arm reached out, grabbing his sleeve with sudden force, and pulling him off balance. Yesod yelled out. He slipped sideways and fell to the wet pavement. The arm

yanked rudely at his thick coat, pulling him into the foreboding dusk of the alley.

"Yer money, I want yer money!" said a voice high and shaky with anger. The attacker jumped quickly on the fallen Yesod trying to find his pant pockets. "Empty yer pockets, now!" He jumped up and down on his victim with a terrible energy, thumping his chest resolutely with frenzied fists, groping for the suit pockets. Yesod thought he was being murdered. He shouted again and again for help, but the streets were momentarily empty of pedestrians. Terror came into his throat, constricting his breathing. The man had come from nowhere.

"Help, help! Get off me, you murderer. Get off, get off. I have no money. I swear to you, no money!" In his fear Yesod shut his eyes and lashed out with all the energy he could muster, squirming to free himself. But the determined little creature hung on, yelling in strange high shrieks while wrestling to get into his victim's pockets. He had enormous energy. His hands groped like motorized claws. Assailant and victim fought like dogs in the darkening gloom, rolling around on the wet, dirty bricks slicked with excrement and rotting garbage.

"Stop it! Stop, I beg you. What are you doing? Who are you?" cried Yesod, grabbing the other man's throat and forcing a confrontation. What he beheld amazed him. His attacker was not some street tough or drug-crazed junkie, but a bald, disheveled, bearded old man!

"I'm yer worst nightmare, that's who! I want yer money, that's all you need to know!" By this time his hairy arms and groping

hands had shoved into Yesod's pockets and come up with keys and loose change, which splattered over the slimy bricks.

"Ah, you faker, you skinflint, where's yer wallet, I want yer wallet!" They wrestled more vigorously.

Yesod, never having been accosted before, fought instinctively to protect himself, but now he began to feel outrage. What had he done to deserve this? How dare he be spoken to this way. A crazy old man at least twice his age. Why pick on him, an innocent, G-d fearing man? He yelled a challenge and joined in the fight with all the vigor he could muster, at last forcing the old man down in the muck.

"Now, you *alta cocker*,[45] I have *you* and the tables are turned! Get up. I'm going to call the police and have you arrested!" Despite his brave words, Yesod was shaking too hard to stand.

The old man tried to roll out of Yesod's grasp, but he was held too tightly. He was beginning to tire, breathing very hard.

Face to face, Yesod looked at his assailant. The hellish figure was short but full bodied. His clothes gave off a foul odor. The crown of his large, bald head was raised to a point, a shiny cap of flesh. Long dirty white hair circled the back of his head and cascaded in front of his large ears toward his heaving chest. His brown eyes were intense and piercing. His nose was a reddened, protruding bulb, its capillaries flushed and swollen. Yesod scowled at this spectre sent to fleece him. Or maybe this was the devil in

[45] Old fool

person. Then the stranger began to chant something unintelligible beneath his ragged breath.

"You're a *dybbuk!*"[46] Yesod shouted. "Evil spirit, G-d save me from you, evil thing!"

Suddenly the old man's eyes widened. He was not looking at Yesod, but at the rain and blackness beyond him. What was there? He let out a loud, high-pitched scream of true fear, as if *he* had seen an apparition in the night. The force of it nearly knocked Yesod off of him.

"You," he cried, trying lustily to free himself. "You will die! I see it. Death, it's coming. *Vay is mere!* A corpse! Let me up! Let me up, I tell you!"

"What the . . . ! What are you talking about? I'm turning you in to the police, you *dybbuk,* you evil old beggar!" Yesod began to pull the man to his feet. He looked around for rope or some means to tie the creature's hands and feet, but it was too murky to see clearly. His captive was pulling out of his grasp with incredible new strength as though fighting now for *his* life.

"Look, I don't want yer money now, just let me up, let me out of here! Yer gonna die, I see it! And not by any hand but yer own. *By no hand but yer own!*" With a sudden wrench to the side the old man freed himself from Yesod's grip and gained his legs. Seconds later, he was running down the alleyway. He vanished into the

---

[46] Evil spirit, demon

obscure night that had spawned him, beard flapping, screaming "*Gevult, gevult!*[47] Death! Death of life!"

Yesod fell back, seized with shock and confusion at the man's strange words. He sat there a long time in the muck, exhausted, in a stupor. Some time later a kind woman passerby found him and helped him to his car. The whole incident had taken less than seven minutes but Yesod, who knew that both good and malevolent forces were always at work in the universe, accepted it as an omen. When he stopped shaking enough to gather himself together, he headed at once for the synagogue.

[47] Fear, astonishment, cry for help

CHAMESH

(Five)

Yesod fished out his keys at the door of *B'nai Israel.* As a permanent, senior member of the *minyan*, his privilege was a key. Rain blew inside the darkness as he quickly shut the massive door behind him. Knowing the light switch was across the room Yesod moved sightlessly toward it, hands outstretched. After bumping into the *Kaddish* table and the coat rack, which hit the floor like an echoing bullet, he flipped on the switch and with the aid of light opened the sanctuary doors. There, ahead in the soft yellow glow of the *Ner Tamid* he grabbed a *yarmulke* from the box at the entry and hurried through the aisles to take his accustomed seat before the *Torah* ark, shivering with cold and fear, mumbling epithets to the memory of his assailant.

"Eternal One," he began in earnest, affixing the *yarmulke* on his head, "Maker of all things holy, You have led us out of Egypt

and given us Your covenants. May Your Name be blessed and exalted, our King, continually. *Amayn*. Almighty One, I am a small man, only one man. Nothing in Your eyes, Eternal One. Thank You for my life. Shielded in Your house, Lord, I am overcome with joy and peace."

Praying in the quiet of the vast, empty room he began to feel better. *At least I'm safe here*, he thought, *maybe the joy and peace will come*. Slowly his trembling ceased, but his worry persisted, and he fell into deep thought over the words of the stranger. "Death, death in life" rang like a maddening song in his head until he moaned and sank down in his seat. "What will I do," he cried out, head in hands, and then he began softly to sob.

"G-d in Heaven, I don't want to die. I want to live. It's a curse! Suicide, it's a worse curse than murder! I'm a peaceful man. What do I know from murder and suicide? Who was that crazy man? Take my own life? Forbid it, forbid it!"

Yesod rocked himself, wishing he had never gone to Ali's, berating himself for holding in his hands the New Testament. Suddenly into his memory came the old framed picture of the man, the Jew, in supplication beside the olive tree. Yesod remembered the way the light fell on his face, his earnest appearance and the yearning in his eyes. Who was he? Did he, Yesod, look like that in prayer? He rose from his chair and moved to the end of the aisle. Assuring himself that no one else was in the room, he bent on one knee, clasping his hands before him. Then raising his eyes to the flickering candlelight, Yesod arranged himself in what he thought was the same pose as the figure in the painting. *Like this*,

he thought, seeing himself robed in white beside the olive tree. He imagined then a lucent beam of light caressing his upturned face. He felt in empathy with the unknown image. In this humble pose, he resumed his prayers.

"G-d in Heaven, what have I done to bring this upon myself? Please, I want only to marry my Sofia Tiferet, to live as a *mensch*, and raise a son to carry on my name, daughters to give us grandchildren. Hear me, Almighty One. All I should think but didn't think, all I should do but haven't done, whatever I said that I should know not to say, *vay is mere*, I am blind. My good deeds they are not enough, forgive me, my *mitzvot* is nothing, *oy, oy, oy* . . ."

It seemed to Yesod that his spirit was not in his body but that it floated above him, mixing itself with the dry air of the huge room. He felt as if a great force had somehow parted his life down the middle, but he could not understand what had changed. He thought of the teachings of *Kabbalah*. He concentrated on the image of the Pillar of Righteousness, a path of purity reaching from earth to the Infinite. If not for a righteous man, it would consume the earth. He thought of a column of clouds congealing and moving upward like some monstrous white tornado, moving and swaying with the sins of the world. No, that must not happen!

"The devout, they sustain the world," he shouted into the void around him. "Without the righteous no world can endure! We are the foundation! I will not fear the Evil One. Hear me, my G-d. I

have the power of *Torah*, of *Halakhah*.[48] I will sustain the world with *Torah!*"

Yesod's triumphant cry rang out. He heard it jump across every seat and reverberate from every wall, coming back to him a host of echoes, as though he were everywhere at once. "My name is Chai," he said to the whirlwind in his brain. "Chai Eleazer. Life! Life itself!"

While driving home that night, it occurred to him that he had never before knelt in prayer. A Jew bends only the neck. "So never tell anyone," he said aloud to the rain.

---

[48] Jewish law, the Law of Moses

SHISHAH

(Six)

Yesod held his tongue and told no one of his encounter in the alley. But his normally quiet sleep was restless and broken with thoughts and fears of death, and he worried that incarnate evil, called by Jews the "Other One," was still hounding him. The prophecy of his impending death worried and confused Yesod. Nevertheless he told himself to be calm and brave, and by the end of the following week he felt more assured. He even began to feel as though the attack was a sort of badge he had won against the onslaught of evil. He met as usual with Gevurah and Hesed in his home after *Shabbat* services. Gevurah was eager to tell the others about his cousin, Levi.

"A fool he is, a *schleimeil.*[49] How can I let this man in my house

[49] Foolish person, unlucky, unfortunate

when he turns against his own people?" Gevurah took a tortured sip of coffee and bit into a strudel.

Hesed tried to cheer his friend. "He didn't actually change anything, Gevurah. He just went to a few meetings. So he's a curious man. That doesn't mean he'll join. Give him a *bissel* time to think it over. How can he leave behind *Torah*? It's a *living thing!*" He laughed in enjoyment at his profundity and pounded the white *Shabbat* tablecloth to make his point.

Gevurah would not be comforted. "Not only *Torah*, but he forgets *mitzvot*, the law. He says to his wife, 'I am going to see my friends,' and he is seen instead going into a church for a meeting of *goyim!* Hannah is already packing, the children are afraid to go to school, and he's not even shamefaced! That *galut*. My cousin!

"I remember before he had children and worried about his business he used to recite a portion of the *Mishnah* and identify the rabbi who wrote it. His whole house was a *bet midrash*."[50] Hesed reached for another strudel and munched happily.

"Why did he go to that meeting?" Yesod asked with great curiosity, not forgetting his own talk with Ali the previous week. "What led him to it, a book, maybe?"

Gevurah turned to Yesod with contempt in his face. "A book? No book can change a man. It was his manager in the factory. He starts telling Levi about how the *Mashiach* is on earth, can you imagine? Right here on earth. Week after week he tells this to my

---

[50] House of study

cousin Levi until finally the dumb *schleimeil* starts to believe him and he has to see for himself."

"What happened?" Yesod asked. "Did he? See, I mean. What was the hoax?"

"The whole thing was a hoax. Just a lot of people claiming to be descended from tribes of Israel. Then they gave him some book about Jews coming to the Americas and told him to pray about it. G-d forbid! He says he asked who the *Mashiach* was and someone told him it was Jesus Christ! But Jesus was nowhere to be seen. So Levi goes home and cries to himself he's been deceived. Hannah finally got it out of him." Gevurah paused for breath and stared into Yesod's face, as if searching for an answer. Hesed reached across the strudel plate to pat his friend's hand in an effort to console him.

"Now, now, Gevurah, he's a grown man, making his own choices. He's Jewish for life. Nothing will change that. Even Jesus Christ can't change it. Even if he denies it, how many others will remind him? Levi could never be a . . . a *meshugah* Christian. Never can he be at peace outside the synagogue. A phase. It's just a phase."

Gevurah harumphed. "That's what *you* think. The next week, and this is where he's a danger to all of us—he goes back for more and comes home smiling! This time he doesn't hide it. He says he was told by something called a "holy ghost" that the book is true. How can this be? Whoever heard of such a thing? Why? What is he looking for he doesn't already have? Why would he bring this shame on his family?"

Gevurah's usual staid demeanor crumbled.

"The image of Levi standing in a congregation of Christians who worship Jesus is an unbearable yoke upon my heart."

He felt sick. He pushed back the chair and slumped onto the green chintz couch. There was silence as each man contemplated the deed that Levi had perpetrated upon his birthright.

Hesed said, "There can be nothing but *Elohim*,[51] Isaiah tells us. Our only judge is *Elohim*. How can there be contradiction, a want for something else? Is the Eternal One not absolute? How can a Jew go looking for what isn't there?"

"He cannot," said Gevurah, sitting up and looking very wise and sad. "He looks for *Mashiach*. *Oy*, can he find the *Mashiach* in a church? Better he should look for the needle in the haystack. First Elijah must come, Israel must have peace and observe *Halakhah* without interruption from the world. Where is peace and prosperity, I ask you?"

"We have never known it!" Hesed slapped his thick hand on the table. "We wait not for a man but for a *kingdom*, a king with the spirit of *Elohim* resting upon him, a David. This David alone will take us to Heaven. Did Jesus Christ do that? No, he was executed, a common criminal, and violence and war have been his gift to us. Poor Levi, the fool."

Their bearded faces bobbed like three sad goats. Yesod stood and walked to a bookshelf beneath the cookie jar and took out

---

[51] One of the names of God

Binah's *Torah*, the one she carried with her from Russia. He turned the frail leaves to Deuteronomy 18:18. He read:

> *I will raise them up a Prophet from among their brethren, like unto thee, and will put my words in his mouth . . .*

"What is that?" Gevurah asked sharply. "What prophet?"

Hesed put down his coffee and looked quizzical.

"Here in Deuteronomy. Moses. ' . . . *and he shall speak unto them all that I shall command him*.' This *Mashiach* will be a prophet. What did you say is the name of *their* gentile prophet?"

"Since *Moishe*?[52] There have been many prophets. They're all dead now. How should I know the name of that *goy*?"

"But the presence of the Eternal One is within us," Yesod said softly to the others, reading now in Hosea 13. "*Torah* gives us the laws, but where is the spirit of those laws? The *Sheckinah*, the presence of the Almighty, provides the feeling of love we have for *Torah*, for the Almighty One. This descendent of David of whom you speak, Hesed, our *Mashiach*, must be one who brings with him that spirit of peace. For some time now I have felt there is a reality we cannot see, mysterious, hidden from us—"

Hesed laughed out loud. "Yesod, you and your *Sheckinah!* Where is this thing, in the air, in the house?" He looked for validation at Gevurah who was lost in his own thoughts.

Yesod turned and put the open book on the table. "Sometimes

---

[52] Moses

I feel a presence," he began again, recalling past *Shabbat* services and the strange whiteness that settled for a moment in the sanctuary. "It's like, like a peacefulness almost, I think to say, a joyful feeling. He is near then, this Presence. Something added, like maybe I'm meeting a *malakh.*"[53] The looks on his companions' faces made him stop.

"An angel? Yesod meets now with angels?" said Hesed. "You better put away your *Kabbalah!* And what does Sofia Tiferet think of such things?"

Yesod didn't answer.

Gevurah rose from the couch and paced up and down the carpeted room. Finally he stopped before the fireplace and looked at the *Hanukkah menorah*[54] on the mantle.

"We cannot wait for *Mashiach*s to come and save us. There is nothing magical about *Torah*. Our duty as Jews is to make *this* world a heaven and a safe place, so the Eternal One can come here and dwell among His people. There is *Halakhah*, the way of the Eternal One, the way Moses was commanded to teach. Each house, a *bet din*, house of judgment, a *bet midrash,* house of study, a *bet tifilah,* house of prayer. Our rabbi is our prophet for now. He reminds us of our duty to study *Torah, Mishnah, Talmud*. What can be more perfect? The entire world is *Torah*. *Elohim* sits in heaven and studies it with us. He wears existence upon Him like

---

[53] A holy angel

[54] Candelabra. The Sabbath menorah has seven branches and an eighth (*shammes*-servant) lights the seven. The Passover candelabrum has eight branches and a *shammes*.

a garment. Who are we to look within His garment?"

Yesod said "Peeling away the layers will bring us to the very core of the Perfect One. Should we not long to know the perfection of G-d through contemplation?"

"That's absurd, Yesod." Gevurah shot back. "Folly. It leads to madness. Where in *Torah*, in *Mishnah*, in *Halakhah* does it say we should search until we find Him? A good way to get burned, to be destroyed. We should know *Hassan*? We might as well be gods ourselves!"

He laughed with derision at the thought and picked up his hat to leave. Hesed took the cue and the rest of the strudel, which he forced into his pockets.

"Me, too, Yesod. Good *Shabbos* to you. Next week, G-d willing, I will have a canvas for you!"

They bid their host *shalom aleichem* and departed for their own homes, touching a kiss to the *mezuzah* at the door as they passed. Yesod dutifully put away his mother's *Torah* and cleaned up the dishes. He was glad to be a Jew. He went upstairs to study again in *Kabbalah* his portion for the evening, and while he read, into his mind came again the quiet gentle face of the man in the painting he had seen in Ali's store. The image stayed with him throughout his study. It calmed him, and he slept well that night, feeling strangely at peace with himself about everything.

Ali was putting pennies he'd found on the street into one of his many jars when Yesod walked in three weeks later with a

bundle of books under his arm. He had carefully avoided taking the usual path to the bookstore but trembled nevertheless as he reached the neighborhood.

"Ah, so you are back again, like a set watch. More books?" He peered through the coat creases of Yesod's arms to see the titles.

Yesod walked to Ali's far counter and deposited the bundle. "Come and see for yourself if you want them. They come from my finest stock." He turned to Ali, keeping his face straight and watching him seal the cap on the filled jar. "Ali, why not a *mitzvot* before Allah? Give away all your captured pennies and dimes so people can buy food with them. You're preserving half the world's change in those bottles!"

Ali acted as if he had not heard. Like a curator of rare artifacts he carefully set the bottle back behind the counter with the others.

"This is a fund for you, Yesod Chai Eleazer, for your marriage! Three months and you will be a married man. Think of it. You will have a bit of dowry from the Arab Ali." Turning to Yesod he winked a brown eye. "What have you brought me here?" He walked to his counter and began untying the bundle.

Yesod hesitated, then walked to the far end of the store. When he had found the picture he sought, he stood in silence before it. He felt almost relieved, and this feeling disturbed him. The light, the face, the figure against the thick, anchoring olive tree, they were already in his memory. Now he saw other things. His eyes first picked out the quality of the white filmy light from the misty darkness, touching the tree but laying like a mantle upon the thin shoulders of the praying man.

Then Yesod looked at the stranger's countenance and began to discern the strength in the features. He noticed the firm set of the mouth, the intense concentration of the eyes as they seemed to penetrate the light. He sensed a life force behind the total figure that was, even in repose, commanding. *He has endured much*, Yesod thought. *Hunger and cold, even loneliness and loss. An Essene perhaps, a poor hungry traveler along Judean desert routes*. But this man did not seem lost to poverty. In his lifted face was a single-minded attention, earnest in every detail. Yesod's eyes moved to the supplicant's folded hands, they were the hands of a craftsman or an artist. Ah, he was an artist without work, a wandering soul, pledged to record the world's beauty in fineness of detail. Yesod smiled. This was a man sensitive to all of life, offering his thankfulness to the Almighty in prayer at day's first light, a common practice among the devout of Jewish men.

"Yesod, where are you?" called Ali from across the store. "These are wonderful books you have brought me. Come and have a fig tart."

Yesod stood a moment longer, his gaze fixed upon the earnest and handsome face of the man in the portrait. Again he traced the light path across the top of the picture, wondering at its source. It cannot be the sun, Yesod thought, those rays are meant only for him, as if he is *part* of the light. He noticed the strength in the tree trunk, it seemed a kind of altar before the praying man. A feeling of peacefulness seemed to emanate from the picture and the Jew who stood beholding his fellow within the framed picture sensed a bond, an ancient kinship he had never felt, even for his father.

Yesod thought suddenly of the white haze that sometimes formed across the synagogue during *Shabbat*. Then he thought of the *Sheckinah*. How alike was the feeling that came to him at these times. A sweet song from somewhere long forgotten was in his ears, disturbing his concentration. *I know you*, his mind whispered to the man in the portrait. *I have seen you, somewhere, somewhere . . .*

"Yesod! Where are you? Ah, I see. At that painting again." Ali came to stand beside him. "You like that picture. Why don't you buy it?"

"Buy it? It's just a Jew praying. Why I should I buy it?"

Ali laughed out loud and gripped his arm around Yesod's shoulder. "This is not 'just' a Jew, Yesod Chai. This is a portrait of Allah's great helper and hero of the New Testament. You know who I mean. This is Jesus Christ."

Yesod caught his breath. "What?" His chest froze in the act of drawing breath. Pulling quickly away from Ali and the portrait, he moaned as if in pain. He felt seduced, betrayed by his own feelings by the sudden catch in his throat.

"Jesus Christ? *This* is him? My G-d in heaven, I've been tricked! I've been fooled! I thought . . ."

"You thought it was some poor nobody? Yesod, what an innocent you are. Surely you knew. There are paintings of him everywhere! This one has been here a long time. How can it hurt to look?"

"To look? Why should I look at him? I'm a Jew, I've been taught better. Jesus Christ, of all people, how could I know?" He

fought for control, his anger mixed with surprise and not a little disappointment.

Ali laughed at his friend. "You are more than what you are taught, my friend. It's just a painting. I got it for a good price. It's beautiful, don't you think? Just look at its colors."

Yesod looked again at the painting. *So this is him*, he thought, wanting not to care. Not an artist, but a carpenter, not a king of Judah, nor a fearsome warrior, but a poor, simply clad soul praying in a garden in the mist of morning. This was the face of the Christian Messiah that lures so many Jews away from synagogue?

He recalled the many twelfth and thirteenth century Italian representations he'd seen of this man in the art books in his store. There was David, Giotto, Michelangelo, Rembrandt, and how many sculptures? Jesus was usually portrayed in ingenuous death upon an ornate cross or crucifix, in paintings and frescoes so stylized they resembled icons or coats of arms. They depicted the poor man adorned in death with blood large as rose petals dripping from his hands and feet, splashing upon backgrounds of treated canvas, wood, clay, and alabaster. A circular halo of gold patina usually embellished Jesus' resigned head, while legions of weeping Italianate saints and floating angels with lavishly drawn wings on their backs mourned in tableau at his feet. To Yesod these pictures were patently unreal, like messages from another planet, and he could not seriously imagine such a creature dwelling upon the earth, much less walking among the poor or teaching *Talmud*. They were merely constructs, the commissioned tales of

overworked imaginations. He had often shaken his head over their maudlin excess. Except for Yesod's knowledge of history and experiences with anti-Semitism, he had no good reason to believe Jesus had ever lived.

Except for this.

This portrait was startlingly different, it might have been a photograph of a real person caught in a private moment of communication with his Maker. No icon was portrayed on this canvas, no sacrificial reminder was evident. This could be a man like any other, real, approachable, *actual.* Yesod sighed heavily. Ali was right, this was not a picture to mock. There seemed a solidarity to this meditating figure that brought Yesod a feeling of respect. Light and energy of will radiated from him. Here was a man in his time. Yet who would claim him as the *Mashiach*? Yesod doubted he would even draw a crowd, much less a devoted following. Then something Gevurah had said came again to his mind. *We cannot wait for Mashiachs to come and save us.* What was there, then, about this Jesus that others followed him? What did they know that he, Yesod, did not? Had *Mashiach* already come?

"Ali," said Yesod aloud. "I have seen all I want. I will have that fig and then I must go to Sofia. She is taking me on a date with her mother."

"That's nice," said Ali in his cryptic Arabic way as he led them to the food.

SHEVAH

(Seven)

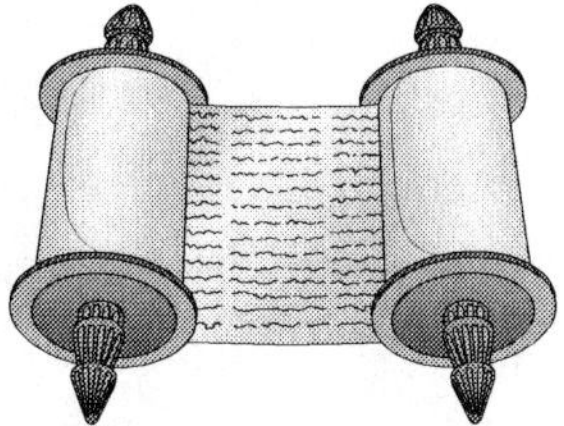

Their date was pleasant. They danced at the Jewish Community Center and mingled with aging *B'nai Brith* women wriggling with effort to old '70s and '80s tunes. Afterward, Yesod drove Sofia and her mother home. They sang Hebrew songs. Esther made them all Sandman tea and finally went upstairs with a cautioning glance at her daughter.

"Half an hour," she said with a small smile. She looked hard at Yesod.

"Then there's time for a thirty minute kiss. *Shalom, Mamale*."

Sixty minutes later Yesod hugged Sofia to him one last time and walked outside to his car. Their wedding, less than eight weeks away, was set for the Sabbath night following Sofia's birthday. They would soon begin the search for an apartment in

the more well to do neighborhood near her parents' home. Yesod was caught up in the excitement of these new experiences, but he had been feeling moments of distraction, times when his mind wandered to Ali's store. At these times he would find himself remembering the expression on Jesus' face or wondering about the singular white light that illuminated that praying figure in the Garden. He had not told Sofia of his encounter with the portrait, and now, as they said their goodnight, he berated himself for holding back.

"Yesod, wait a *bissel*."

Yesod turned and Sofia came down the porch steps and into his arms once more. Her perfume was enticing, he held her tight and breathed it against the warmth of her neck.

"Yesod, tell me you love me." She clung to him.

"I adore you, my precious, my wife-to-be. How can you question it?" They moved in unison together in the wind for a long moment. He felt her relax against him and knew this was right. They belonged together.

"I was a little worried, *Chaili*, that's all. You seemed distracted tonight, even *Mamale* noticed." She stroked his short beard, pulling gently at the hairs to tease him.

"Nothing to worry about, nothing at all. Just thoughts of business. Nothing, nothing." Now would be a good time, he thought. They were alone. They could discuss it uninterrupted.

Sofia looked relieved. She smiled at him, her black eyes shining with happiness. "Business," she said coyly. "I will be your business,

Chaili. We will make some business soon enough."

"*Not* soon enough!" he said. "Every day, every hour is pain!"

They laughed together and she left him after a while, giggling at his desire.

Once home Yesod relaxed for a time on the chintz couch, thinking of his good fortune and coming marriage. Already the preparations were being made through his mother and Esther, Sofia's mother. There was little for him to do until the building of the *huppah* but find an apartment and a tuxedo. Humming to himself he poured a small glass of grape wine and went upstairs to reread a chapter of *Kabbalah*. Yesod greatly valued these excerpts from texts that originated in Palestine before the sixth century. Thoughts of Sofia left him as he settled in and became absorbed in the esoteric of *sefirot*, the name given to numerical entities that attempt to catalogue the lights, powers, and attributes of G-d through a list of ten classic mystical manifestations leading to wisdom.

Yesod reviewed again the ancient tree of tradition that traces the path to self-knowledge and knowledge of G-d. Beginning at the top he first contemplated the idea of nothingness, the primordial condition that preceded the creations the Eternal One brought into being. Second, the Master endowed mankind with life. When coupled with wisdom the attributes of power and love came into being. From these flow emanations of beauty and compassion. A soul enlightened in this way is most capable of living every

moment in the splendor of bountiful blessings. He might even be moved to prophesy. This line of meditation eventually led Yesod through other thoughts on qualities possessed by G-d. He contemplated the idea of *Malkhut*,[55] the melding of beauty, love and spirit that, to the Hebrew wise men of early centuries, represented the idealized union of male and female. They taught that a fully meaningful life is attainable only when universal forces are operating as one flowing unity through the foundation of all things, the life force, the seat of passion, the fountain of eternal renewal through which the seeds of creation are manifest, the male member, the life force on earth.

Therefore, Yesod read, the world is not static because these forces are always influencing all that a man does and will do. But what is the original and final power, the hidden spark of eternal combustion that lights the torch of life? Ah, it is the "orchard of existence" of which ancient sages wrote, the *Sheckinah*, G-d's force field of continual energy, His mysterious unseen Presence.

Yesod loved the *Kabbalah*. It gave him a feeling of closeness to his Creator. Sometimes, in his mind's eye he saw strange bursts of light before him, and he thought that spirits of the dead might be passing through the air he breathed. Sometimes he imagined he knew a bit of the inner life of G-d, that he had uncovered hidden aspects of the Divine personality. He felt it a duty as a Jew to understand these things, hoping to venture deeper into contemplation of sacred things and to partake of this spirit that

[55] From Hebrew "melek," king. Malkhut means kingdom

would bring him nearer the Presence of G-d.

Studying about the *Sheckinah* always led Yesod's thoughts back to Sofia, as if his religious life was incomplete without her, as though he were linked forever to both her and *Kabbalah.* Now he sat quietly with eyes shut and meditated upon all that he had studied. He tried to forget himself totally, to transcend time, space, and thought, hoping G-d would clothe Himself in him. "Come into me," he said to the eternal cosmos beyond the constraining skin of his room, beyond the quiet night of stars. "I am a part of all that is and is to be."

He waited many minutes, trying not to be lulled asleep, hoping to be a channel for the Divine. In a moment he smiled. It was beginning. The Eternal One never sleeps, and He fills the mind of man with His secrets. Blessed be He. Then it was there again. Yesod squinted a look.

A faint white haze had come into the room, twisting slowly before him, moving back and forth just beyond sight. Slowly it began to change, taking a shape. At first it was only a small light, but gradually the haze appeared to solidify. In its whiteness, Yesod beheld the faint outline of a man at the edge of his room, no more than a dozen feet from him, in a now familiar praying position upon his knees. The image grew clearer. Yesod held his breath. In another moment, the figure assumed a reality of size and shape, his body becoming solid. This figure of a man, now real as any other, rose to his feet.

Yesod gasped and held his breath. He could not see the man's face for the light that enveloped it but suddenly wanted to fall to

his knees. The man now turned slowly toward Yesod with tender yearning. *I am he whom thou seekest*, the man said softly but firmly, in a clear, modulated tone. *Come follow me*. The personage did not move, but met Yesod's startled eyes for a long instant. Then he simply turned and disappeared as through a doorway, taking the brilliant light with him. The room fell into shadowed darkness again. All was as before.

Yesod sat still as stone, unable to react or even to think. From a place in himself that he did not know, something seemed to move slowly toward his heart, like a gentle but firm rush of unaccountable energy. He was overcome with astonishment! A feeling prompted him to look above, and there Yesod beheld another phenomenon. It was a funnel of the whitest light descending to conform its luminance around *him*. Was he imagining that this light came through the ceiling? He blinked hard and rubbed his eyes, hoping to see again the personage who had spoken to him, but this new brilliance was blinding.

Finally, Yesod's whole body became enveloped in intense luminosity. He shut his eyes against the glare. A feeling of love washed over him, pure love and joy. Then a languid peacefulness overtook him, relaxing and quieting the threshold of his mind, and he felt it flow into his heart. His spirit was being fed. Yesod opened his eyes. A knowledge came quietly to his spirit. The solitary figure of the man had not returned, but his impression was clear, the meaning was undeniable. It was the *Sheckinah!*

Tears came, and sobs, unbidden but copious and urgent. "I am like Moses," he gasped, and he held himself in the wonder and

shock of new understanding. "My G-d, my G-d, I am like Moses." In the midst of his room bathed in new light, Yesod the Jew dropped his book on the floor, fell to his knees, and covered his face in awe.

SHEMONEH

(Eight)

Sleep could not entrap Yesod this night. His brain steamed with thoughts of what he had experienced until he had relived every small detail again and again. He felt alternately joy and awe. He had beheld the Son of G-d. This was real. It was sure. His prayers were heard and answered! He had come, the *Sheckinah!*

Yesod strode the room, pacing it from corner to book-strewn corner. He spoke aloud to himself, laughed, and prayed, and tried to meditate. Alternately he cried, he felt giddy, he stared at the walls, forgetting where he was. He could not read more but eventually fell into a sort of spiritual stupor. In the light of his room he sat propped in the unpadded wooden chair beside his desk, remaining this way in shock, until morning when he arose to go to the bathroom. But his body was weak from excitement and spiritual exertion. He plopped back into his chair trembling,

his legs unsteady, his back sore. In a half hour, he arose again.

He was afraid of what looked back at him in the mirror, a face haggard of thought, brown eyes reddened with staring and still widened in disbelief. His spirit was wild, he felt alternately like dancing and running up and down the stairs of the house shouting, "I have seen him! He is real! *Mashiach! Sheckinah!*"

His tongue was thick. Upon examining his face, he thought he looked astonished, coming into forced contact with his own image. What cannot be, is so. What has been, no longer contains what is. He stared at himself and saw in his dilated pupils the synagogue, the rabbi at the podium reading *Halakhah*. He heard the long, pleading wails at *Yom Kippur*, the yearly Day of Atonement, his own tears falling like guilty wet bodies to the floor. Through the mist that now formed, bathing his eyes in a dew of confused remembrances, the stanchions of Yesod's sheltered life passed before him: the flickering candles of hundreds of *Shabbat*s, the six-pointed Shield of David on the wall of his room, the *Torah* ark in synagogue where, from his place before it, he had countless times recited the *Shema*. *Hear, O Israel, the Lord is One,* with pride and certainty that *there is no Other*.

But there was another, overlooked and cast out by his own kind.

What was he to do? He thought of Sofia, his betrothed. She was a devoted Jew, completely happy with the teachings of *Torah*. Could he confide in her his experiences with the *Sheckinah*? Would she think him mad? His parents, they would disown him, surely. Rabbi Schechter? Gevurah? He could see his friend sternly staring

needles of barely repressed condemnation at him.

I am alive, I am dead, he thought, feeling lighter and at the same time a strange heaviness of responsibility, as though he had just hosted a guest who brought with him a world. *I am he whom thou seekest. Come follow me*. Those words touched his searching heart. They would change his life forever, he knew, but beyond that he did not understand.

With a trembling energy he showered and dressed and fought an urge to wake Binah. He walked out of his mother's house forgetting to touch the *mezzuzah*[56] on the door lintel and unsure for the first time in his life, who he was.

Coming again to the dark alleyway near Ali's store, the fateful, almost forgotten words of the *dybbuk* came back to Yesod with such force that he nearly fell over faint. *'Yer gonna die, I see it! No hand but yer own!'*

"*Oy, gevult*, I forgot, I forgot," he said aloud. "My death!" He ran back to his car and hid his head in his coat. Ali found him there later while looking for change on the sidewalk.

"What are you doing here, Yesod?" asked Ali, helping his friend out of his car and shepherding him into the store. "Are you sick, throwing up? Here, come in. I have sweet figs to make everything come out all right." He held Yesod against his new dark suit contrasted by a svelte new red and gold tie. Yesod

[56] Small oblong container on front door lintel of Jewish homes containing scroll with citations from Leviticus

grabbed his briefcase, heavy with a bargaining tool, the idea for which had come to him during the night.

"I don't want your figs. Nothing will help, I'm all right, leave me be."

The two reached the desk chairs and Ali deposited Yesod heavily in one and took the other.

"All right, Mr. Chai Eleazer, what's the problem with you? You break up with your girl what's her name Sophie?"

"Sofia Tiferet is fine, at least for now. It's nothing like that yet. It's different, it's . . . the picture, the one in the corner against the wall."

Ali's eyes widened, his mouth dropped into his long beard. He looked suddenly to Yesod like some ancient Hebrew rabbi on his way through Jerusalem to High Holy Day services, except for the gold tie tack that bore the legend "Allah King" in Aramaic script.

"The portrait? The one of Jesus Christ?"

"That one."

"What about it? It's making you sick?"

"It's not making me sick. It's calling me. It speaks to me."

Ali stared at Yesod, his mind trying to comprehend the painful confession, but he only dimly perceived the dilemma.

"I want to buy it," Yesod said, staring into the stacks vaguely. "I want to buy that picture."

Ali assessed his friend for a time. "You want the picture? Yesod

the Jew is buying a picture of Jesus Christ?" His voice was soft but a trifle teasing. He was working on the possibilities.

Yesod, his face contorted with the effort of trying not to show his need, turned to face Ali. "How much?" Yesod asked, hating now even the thought of having to bicker with this Arab about something newly holy to him. He wanted to run over and look again at the face uplifted in solemn and trusting prayer, grab it, and run. But he knew he mustn't reveal his emotions.

"How much I want for it? You're asking me to sell you a picture you refused even to look at? 'I'm a Jew,' you said, 'What would I want with a picture of Christ?'"

"Don't *hak a chainik*,[57] Ali! The past is gone. Now is another day. How much for the picture?"

"That portrait did not come easy, you know, Yesod. I got it from an old Chinese in Queens who got it from an estate sale. He paid good money, and I paid him more."

"Ali, you told me yourself it was just another picture. What did you pay? Five dollars, ten?"

Ali laughed. He stood up and walked in a circle and came back and sat down.

"You insult me. You think I'm a fool, Yesod, that I get merchandise at flea markets? Such a lovely portrait, very inspiring, in perfect condition, the colors bright, even there is no dust on it. Come and we'll look in a new light."

---

[57] Talk nonsense

Ali stood and walked resolutely to the back wall of his store near the morning light streaming through the windows, his expensive black shoes giving off applied sheen. Yesod stood and followed slowly, wanting and not wanting to see the face he now recognized as his *Mashiach*. How could he bear this new delay?

Ali reached the portrait and gave the sculptured wooden frame a proprietary brush.

"Yes, a lovely thing. It's not cheap, you know. It could hang in any church just like it is. Look here at the textures, the light and dark, *chiaroscuro*. I hear that is the look of Israel in the morning sun. I have been to Israel, Yesod. Me, Ali, an Arab. You have not been there, to your own homeland?"

"Cheap shot, Ali." This was torturous. He could see himself with the portrait, rushing from the store to his waiting car. A blanket would cover it until it rested safely out of sight in his storeroom. There it was, bright in the daylight halo of early winter light, the portrait of a Jew, who with words of truth persuaded a multitude to arise from the despair of toil and slavery and follow him. *You still lead those who will hear your voice*, Yesod's heart spoke to the portrait. He became calm, happy to see again this face he was learning to love. As he gazed and Ali talked, Yesod somehow knew that he had been led to this spot by the power of G-d. He smiled.

"Ah," said Ali, again stroking his beard to a point just below his tie clip. "He makes you smile now? Yesod, you are in great trouble, you know that." His prophetic words hung in the air like a shroud. Yesod shivered involuntarily, dreading the truth behind them.

"Just tell me, what do you want? I have other errands, you think I came here to bicker? I'll give you twenty-five, not a cent more." Yesod avoided Ali's eyes. Starting the bidding would maybe hasten the procedure, he reasoned. He wanted to get the painting to his store where he could carefully hide it before Sofia visited.

Ali laughed as though he had just heard a child's innocent joke.

"A mere twenty-five? What do you take me for? You, my friend. I tell you honestly, I paid much more for this very desirable portrait of Allah's helper. I would have to charge you one hundred for it, and only because we are businessmen." He looked benignly at his Jewish friend. Yesod sensed Ali's hope of easy victory, his anxiety increasing.

"A hundred? That's robbery! More than forty you couldn't have paid at the very most. Probably you weaseled it from that Chinese antique dealer who had no idea what he was looking at! Forty is plenty, forty it is." Yesod turned on his heel, shoved his hands in his pants pockets and walked away from the painting as if to get the money from his briefcase.

Ali came up behind him. "One hundred is nothing for a perfect picture like that. It's not a copy. It's original! Think of what the artist went through to create that. He was inspired, Yesod, appointed to do this work. Is this the respect you give him, and me, your friend?"

"I think your respect ends at the money in your hand, Ali, I—"

Ali's face flushed, angered by Yesod's flippant attitude. The men faced each other, oblivious to the world, hands in pants pockets, neither willing to move. Outside, traffic was increasing in the streets, and people were looking in the store windows. There was a long silence.

"Two hundred."

"What? Insane Arab!"

"Two hundred. Double. Double or nothing!"

"Go to hell. Why should I pay you double, you crook?"

"Double. You insult my picture, my store and myself. Double or you leave here now!"

Yesod could hold his temper no longer.

"*Meshugah!* I am the one insulted. To you I come for eleven years, is it? To you I bring my good books, my business? Customers I send you. All I want is that picture in the corner where it has held up the wall gathering dust for years! Double you want? Even wholesale you wouldn't get from me!"

"Then leave here without it. You think I'm a fool? Where are you going to put that thing? Your mother will kill you anyway. *Salaam*, Yesod. Better luck with the rest of your day."

Ali pushed out his chest further. With his ringed fingers, he carefully smoothed his new tie and turned toward his desk. Yesod, fuming, followed Ali. Quietly he picked up his old briefcase, set it down with a bang on the broad counter. There was still a bargain to be made. The lock snapped open.

Ali turned around and stared at the briefcase. "What are you doing? I told you to leave."

Yesod's face was a mask. Slowly he reached inside and pulled out a heavy cotton sack tied at the top. He dropped it on the counter in front of Ali. With another snap he closed his briefcase.

"There. For you. *Faftik*."[58]

Ali stared at the bundle with suspicion. His hairy hands extended to encompass it. It chinked against his fingers. Carefully, trembling more than slightly, Ali undid the knot and peered inside. His eyes bulged. It was full of coins.

"More than a hundred. Enough for a new bottle to stash behind your counters. Take it or leave it, and make up your mind fast because now I take my picture and go."

Ali reached his hand inside and let the newly minted coins run through his fingers. They might have been diamonds. A grin of simple pleasure crossed his face. He held lovingly his new treasure to his heart. Yesod had already crossed the room to the picture of Jesus. Carefully he lifted it. He headed for the door and his car beyond.

"This time we'll call it settled," Ali yelled as Yesod reached the shop door, his eyes still on the coins. "Yesod?"

But Yesod was already out the door and laughing, exploding

---

[58] Enough! We're finished!

with laughter. Held tightly to his heart was the portrait of Jesus Christ praying in the Garden of Gethsemane, his at last.

"*Farschtinkener*," he said out loud to Ali when he was safely in the car and no one could hear him.

TISHAH
(Nine)

Sofia's car was nowhere in sight when Yesod returned to his store. He drove around the corner through the alley to the back door and quickly unloaded the portrait from his back seat. In his mind he had found a spot for it between the wall that separated his little office from the larger warehouse and the back of some shelving that abutted it. Now he hurriedly brought it to this area. Sandwiched in the narrow, dark slot went the booty. He felt like a thief as he heard the front door squeak and heard the lock turn.

"*Shalom*, *Chaili*?" came the lilting voice, sweet as a nightingale's. It floated to him over the book stacks and past the desktop strewn with invoices. "*Tzetzele*, where are you hiding?" she sang. Yesod, thankful that she hadn't come through the warehouse without announcing her presence, hurried out to meet his Sofia.

She threw her young arms around him, her diamond-topped

watch flashing in the dim light. Her body against his brought sudden desire to them both, and they kissed with a passion that surprised him.

"*Chaili*, I found a dress, *the* dress! It's lovely, it's *shayna!* I'll be your beautiful bride in this perfection. Come tonight and see it. Mom found it yesterday and oh, you're sweating, *Chaili!* Are you ill?"

Yesod wiped his arm across his brow, embarrassed at his effusion.

"No, my *shayna*, just lifting and unpacking books the usual . . ." he trailed off, looking at her shining radiance. He needed so to tell her now, while they were alone and could talk about it. She was usually very empathetic about his forays into the arcane and mystical. "They are all a part of G-d's universe," she would say in her placid way, looking past him at perhaps some unseen presence that communicated with her from a respectable distance.

"Sofia, come sit with me. I have something to tell you."

He took her hand and led her to her seat in his office. She walked with him, smiling and smoothing out her silk dress on the narrow bench, arranging her coat beside her. The musky perfume she wore coated the air around them. She reminded Yesod of an innocent, obedient child-woman, sure of being loved and sure that the world basked, as she did, in a happy certainty of balance.

"Sofia Tiferet, something happened to me the other night, in my room. I need to tell you, because this thing that has occurred

I can't yet explain, but . . ." Her attention was completely his. She had no idea what he was about to say. Gently, he took both her hands in his, and with a silent prayer, told her the whole story.

When Yesod finished, he realized Sofia hadn't said a word. She had turned her face toward the far wall of his office so he could only see her profile. He wanted passionately for her to understand. He waited for her reaction, biting his lip nervously.

"Sofia?"

There was no response. She might have been a sculpture sitting there, showing nothing. He felt that, if he at that moment reached out to touch her, he would find her cold as marble. He held back, confused at her silence.

"My darling, I know this is new for you, but—"

Sofia turned to him. He was astonished to see a tear move slowly down her cheek, though no sound came and her face was set hard. She stood suddenly and walked to the entrance of the office to lean against the doorjamb. He watched her slender outline rest there, as if her body and mind was a single perfect unit of motion. No one spoke for several minutes. Yesod hoped Sofia would accept his experience as the miracle he knew it to be.

"You say you have discovered that Jesus Christ is the *Sheckinah*, the holy presence of G-d," Sofia's tone was glacial, as if she were reading from a list of numbers. "You say that this portrait of him became alive in your room, and that you experienced a miracle because he appeared to you in person and spoke directly to *you*, is that right, Yesod?"

Still she did not turn around. Her voice seemed to come from the walls, from the books outside the room, like a bodiless accuser. He felt himself becoming unnerved.

"Yes," Yesod answered truthfully, as though he were guilty of treason. "Yes, it is so." But he felt no regret.

"And you have told me that this Jesus creature *told* you *he* is whom you truly seek, that you should come to *him*, and that you now know, Yesod, that Jesus is the *Mashiach*, the Messiah of the gentiles *and of the Jews*, and that you have purchased the portrait? You have the portrait?"

She turned to face him now as his accuser, her expression newly stern and remote, as though he had already been judged and awaited only the degree of his punishment. Where was his gentle Sofia? A cold chill crept across his chest.

"Yes, yes, Sofia Tiferet. I have it here. Would you like to see it now?"

His voice rose with hope that she would look at the man in prayer beside the tree and her heart would melt as his had done.

"No. You may keep it, but I do not wish to see it, Yesod. What do you intend to do with this portrait?"

She crossed her arms but stayed at a distance from him, quiet and self-contained. Her beautiful face a living frieze, she stared at him. Yesod felt fear in his stomach, trapped by the need to make things right, the ominous evenness of her tone making him shiver. He felt cold sweat in his armpits. Why hadn't he kept his secret until after their wedding?

"I . . . I will take it home, perhaps. I'm not sure. Sofia? What's wrong, my love? Please come to me, Sofia Tiferet. I love you so much."

He held out his arms to her. Sofia didn't move but instead began to walk the room, passing before him as though he were not there. Again, steely silence. Yesod fidgeted, working at small paper cuts that always irritated his fingers the price of opening boxes and handling books. He didn't know what else to say. *Perhaps*, he thought, *she is not yet ready for my earthshaking confession!* In time, in time she would see it. He would teach her.

He reminded himself of her heritage. Her maternal grandfather was a *Sephardic* rabbi in Spain, her father's father a well known Orthodox cantor. Her family had lost hundreds of relatives in the Holocaust, and many had fallen away through intermarriage with gentiles. As a guarantee against her exposure to worldly pressures, Sofia's parents had imbued in her an intense love for all things Jewish and cautioned her to remain true to *Torah* and *Halakhah*. She had never strayed from their teachings or caused them to worry for her devotion. She was a child of The Book.

"I want children, Yesod."

Lost in his own thoughts, he didn't hear her.

"What? Yes, my *shayna*?"

"Children. I want many children."

Her voice had not softened. Yesod thought of his mother's voice, how it became disapproving of him when she meant to have her way.

"Of course, my darling, many children I will give you."

"I want a husband who loves me and who loves his children. We must be his whole life."

Yesod nodded his head. So it was all right, then? She was coming around.

"But we have a problem, Yesod, a problem with priorities."

"Priorities? Something is wrong with my priorities? I love you. I will live and die for you and our children, Sofia, as will you. What could be wrong with my priorities?" He felt like vomiting out his fear. This was new territory, another face. He didn't know the woman who stood like a monolith of ice before him.

Sofia's face tightened, anger beginning to show at the corners of her mouth. She stared at Yesod as if she had discovered him with another woman in the midst of the wedding feast.

She said in a tone he had never heard, "I will not have a Christ lover in my home, Yesod. There is no room in *my* house for a man who loves Jesus Christ."

Yesod was stunned. He had started this, he knew, but he couldn't believe her response! He jumped to his feet, grabbing her by the shoulders, shaking her.

"Sofia Tiferet! It's you I love, with my heart, with my life. This other thing, it's new, I don't know, it's different, like a new peace, a joy in my heart. It's so different from you and me. There's no competition, you don't understand! Sofia, please, there's room for *everything*, please try and understand! No threat, only more—"

But Sofia pulled away and began putting on her coat with the sure strokes of one being fed righteous anger. Yesod went to stop her, but she shook him off, then faced him. Her eyes were live fires. All formalities were dropped.

"How could you betray me, Yesod, your betrothed? What about the love we have for each other? How can you let another come between us? I know what it is. It's that damned *Kabbalah!* The devil's in that book. You'll be damned for that, Yesod. How dare you! You're a Jew. I'm a Jew. Our children must be Jews, *not Christians*, not *Jesus lovers!* Damn you, Yesod. I will not let you bring a curse upon our marriage! In the house of a Jew there is *no room* for Jesus Christ!"

She was almost screaming now, her throat constricted with tears. She left him and ran crying past the silent bookcases out of the store, slamming the door so hard it swung open again.

Yesod started after her, but the look of hatred she threw behind her stopped him. He sank to his knees, distraught and filled with disbelief. *I am dead*, he thought in panic. "What will I do? What have I done?" Sobs tore out of his heart. Suddenly the figure of the *dybbuk* came again to his mind, the accusing black eyes, the devil from nowhere. He trembled anew at the terror-filled words, "By yer own hand!"

"No, no! Go away. Leave me alone!" he yelled at the loathsome image. He pulled himself into a chair near the door and sat there a long time, oblivious of the world. Passers by coming to browse or bargain met with a shut door, and seeing the curled up figure on the chair just inside, politely averted their eyes and

hurried on, perhaps supposing that he was recovering from the result of his vices, those occasional indulgences that are the secret pleasures of bachelorhood.

ASERET

(Ten)

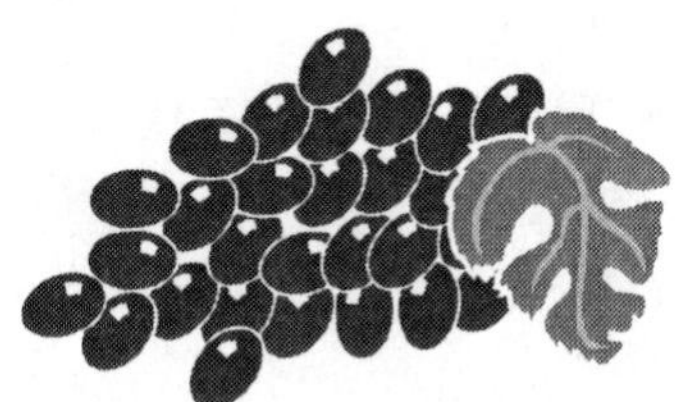

Blustery March came smelling of spring. To Jews it signifies the month of *Pesach*[59] and Binah was already preparing for the Feast week. Though no longer Orthodox, she kept a *kosher* house on major Jewish holidays, her reasons being twofold. "You never know when a new Egypt may appear," she said, wanting to be safe from any wrath of G-d that might afflict her for not remembering His marvelous saving of Israel from slavery more than thirty centuries past.

Binah's second reason was more personal. Her father, Moishe, the fishmonger insisted that his small family observe this day holy to all Jewry. She remembered him stomping into the small kitchen

---

[59] Equivalent to Passover. Festival of Freedom from slavery. Lasts eight days. All leaven is taken from the home until the holiday is over.

three days before the first night of *Pesach* and yelling out to her mother, "Anna, remember the leaven! *Pesach* comes. Go, give it to the *goy!*"

Anna would say "Ja, Ja, Moishe" and gather up her yeast and even her good flour and take it to the shed of her neighbor, Stanislaw the Catholic, until *Pesach* week had passed. This they did every year until they came to America, where Anna had trouble finding non-Jews in her neighborhood. She and Moishe had to rent a locker every year to get it out of their apartment until it was safe to reclaim it. It was their Jewish neighbor, Isaac, who owned the lockers, and every year he made enough *gelt* renting lockers to Jews who observed *Pesach* to buy his large family many presents at *Chanukah*.

Getting ready for *Pesach* was a task that occupied Binah night and day for ten days, two days before the *Seder* meal, and one full day to clean up after the guests. In addition to unpacking the special eight-candle *menorah*, the *Seder* china and utensils, the tablecloth and napkins, there was *matzoh*, shankbone, bitter herbs for *charoseth*, salt, wine, nuts, apples, and so on. There were guests to invite, and charity to be given, never mind the housecleaning that went on morning to night, a ritual purification.

Binah didn't mind the sweeping of dust or washing of curtains in her large home once a year. It was like discarding the past year's disappointments and missed opportunities and opening her life to a new freedom of experience and hope. For these blessings she was grateful, and her housekeeping was equally vigorous. No room in the home was off limits, not even Yesod's den of mystical books.

It hadn't received the blessing of disinfectant since the previous year's holidays. As penalty, she had told Yesod she would not enter his dirty room and for him to do his own cleaning this year. Climbing the stairs, mop and bucket in hand, Binah passed his still cluttered desk and floor.

"Oy, this son of mine lives in a pig sty," she mumbled and decided she would attack the room anyway, in the same manner she approached her work on the city's Beautification Committee.

Her son's retreat was a studied mess. Clothes worn during previous days were piled in a corner, begging for a washday. Paperwork from his store littered his simple oak desk. These were kept captive from blowing out the open window by coffee mugs full of sour *Mogen David* grape, Ovaltine, watered coffee, and grapefruit juice. Four bookcases overflowing with tomes of Hebraica surrounded his desk. Binah laughed. It looked to her like a fortress of dead Yiddish scholars had been called back to life for their profoundest opinions, summoned here to advise and protect Yesod while he studied into the night. An old, very used copy of the *Kabbalah* lay open on the desk. In numerous places the Hebrew text was marked and circled in red pencil.

Binah shrugged. Her son, the devoted mystic. She had often pondered the kind of husband her quiet, reclusive offspring would become . . . and if Sofia Tiferet really understood him. Lately he'd seemed distracted and worried. But Yesod was not one to confide readily to her or to Keter, her husband.

Binah dipped her mop in the Lysol solution and pushed it under the metal-framed bed against the back wall. It struck

something hard. Books under the bed, she thought. Why doesn't Yesod show more respect for his books and—wait! This doesn't feel like books, more like a long flat thing. *Gevult*, now I'll have to move the bed! What could be under there?

Getting on her hands and knees, Binah crawled under the cross-hatched metal framework of the bed and reached out to grasp the object that was interrupting the progress of her mop. It felt like a picture frame. She pulled at it, and a few moments later, she sat on the floor looking at a portrait of a man praying in light filtering through a soft green canopy of leaves.

"What in the world?" Binah said, staring at the thing she'd unearthed.

On the street below, Yesod, the forsaken, was coming home for hot *matzoh* ball soup. He shut the front door against the howling wind outside and shivered. He'd been cold since the argument with Sofia the day before cold and desperately sad. Then, as his ears accustomed themselves to the interior of the house, he realized the screaming in his ears had come from the direction of his room. He suddenly remembered he had earlier that day brought the portrait of Jeshua to his room momentarily, for comfort, remembering his mother had instructed him to clean the place thoroughly for Pesach. He quickly climbed the stairs to the threshold. There sat his mother on the floor, mop handle in lap, crying and rocking to and fro. She saw Yesod and pointed at the found portrait beside her in apparent terror. She pushed it toward him, her face disbelieving, her wide-eyed stare saying it all.

"I can explain, *Momale*," said Yesod, knowing that his explanations would not matter. He stepped inside the room with a heavy sigh and decided he would not tell her about Sofia.

ECHAD-ESRAH

(Eleven)

When Binah emerged from her son's room half an hour later, mop and pail banging on the railing as she angrily descended the staircase, Yesod shut himself in his room with the portrait. In his ears were his mother's portentous words.

"I forbid you to have a picture of this Jesus in my house. Take it immediately out and get rid of it in the alley where Mrs. Feinbein and Councilman Smith won't see it. No Jewish son of mine will be caught praying to a Christian G-d. This is poison. You are a Jew, Yesod. One of the *chosen!* Think of your Jewish identity."

To Yesod's protestations that he prayed only to G-d Himself, Binah answered,

"*It* goes or *you* go, take your choice. Soon it will be *Pesach*,

freedom from slavery for the Jews. How can I present a clean house to G-d on a holy day when my son blasphemes? And what of the congregation? They will disown us all, *oy, oy, oy!*"

Yesod tried reasoning with his mother but to no avail. It was an eerie sequel to the episode with Sofia. He finally sat her down and confessed his strange story to her. His mother asked many questions. Some he couldn't answer, but in the end Binah gave Yesod an ultimatum: twenty-four hours to get rid of the portrait.

"Maybe you're right, maybe wrong, Yesod. I think you've been bewitched. My duty is to protect you from these things. Don't let me hear you've taken it to the store, or to Sofia," she shook the mop at him, her voice an octave higher than usual. "She sees that, you're dead." Binah drew an index finger across her ample throat to illustrate and then wagged it in Yesod's face. "And another thing, why do you read all night *Kabbalah*? See what it brings you? Read only *Torah* and *Talmud*, Yesod. Don't tempt the forces of evil to come into your life."

"Evil? What do you mean, evil? *Kabbalah* was written by Hebrew rabbis, men of impeccable honesty and fervor for the Almighty! These ideas are pondered in *yeshivas*[60] and among the sages of Israel."

"Do they see visions of Jesus Christ? Do they go out and bring home pictures of Christians? Twenty-four hours, Yesod. Make it disappear by tomorrow night."

---

[60] Hebrew universities

Her wisdom and anger vented for the moment, Binah, mumbling apologies to her dead departed relatives, retreated to her kitchen. Yesod was left alone with the portrait to ponder its fate and his own.

It was all so crazy, how lives could be upset by the change of one man's heart. He had only wanted to know more, to delve into the mysteries of his religion, to discover in this life the living power and presence of his G-d. Was it his fault he had been given a miracle?

Yesod looked at the picture lying beside him and ran his fingers along the frame. The face of Jesus was strong and trusting. He knew that look, the yearning of the heart for communion with the unseen Energy, the One who ran the world. He felt it now, and he felt heavily the pressure his choices had brought him. "I am forced to choose," he told the kindly face on the canvas. "I am like Adam, on a precipice between two worlds! If I step forward one inch, my life is finished. I am outcast among my own people! There will be an empty place at the *Seder* table on *Pesach!* And what of my seat in synagogue, for which I paid a handsome price to sit in front?"

Yesod saw himself lying dead in his mother's living room in his only dark suit. He thought of his grandfather, Moishe. How he would cry and tear his clothes, how they would all hold a funeral for him and ask forgiveness for his deceived and wayward soul. The drapes were drawn and the mirrors covered in shame. His parents were weeping around his cheap wooden casket. Sofia wasn't there even to pay respects to the memory of their love.

Only Gevurah the lawyer came by on his way to a rich Jewish client, stopping a moment to look with disdain and indignation at poor Yesod, the *nebbish*,[61] traitor to the faith of Israel's finest sons and forever lost to all things Jewish.

But even as he anguished, Yesod knew that what he had witnessed just a few nights ago in this very room was real. The man known to the non-Jewish world as Jesus, *Jeshua* of old, had come to *him*, the embracing light, the feeling of certainty that washed through him like a silent messenger, filling him with love, peace and joy. *I am he whom thou seekest. Come follow me*. Those words were meant only for him, words of life not death, of hope not despair. *Jeshua*.

There was no going back.

Yesod sighed deeply. He, too, had been blinded, tricked along with countless billions of Jews. But *now!* Fate had brought him to a new depth of understanding, no longer a reader only, he'd seen and heard for himself the power and beauty that had framed the truth in that singular utterance. With every heartbeat, every drawn breath, *he knew! Jeshua ha Mashiach.*

Wait! Maybe there was a way out. He could keep the picture in his store hidden between the boards of his office. It wouldn't be discovered there. Sofia would take him back. He would claim he was temporarily blinded. Their children would be raised as Jews. He could keep his seat in synagogue, and all would be as

---

[61] An unfortunate person, to be pitied

before! He would be a secret believer, a closet Christian. No one would ever know.

He looked again at the white-clad figure, elegant in its simplicity. He marveled at how the gnarled thick trunk offered protection and support to the man whose face was turned to the heavens in firm supplication. He looked hungry for acceptance of his pleas. Was it true that Jesus prayed for all mankind? Was it true? Did this one man save all men from sin and death as Christians claimed?

Perhaps we are kinsmen, Yesod wondered. *Alike in our hunger, we pilgrimage to the feet of the Almighty and open our hearts to the ears of angels, hoping not for judgment but for comfort despite an indifferent world and for knowledge beyond the prideful brotherhood of men*.

He sighed, feeling guilt. He choked, knowing he must not deceive himself or Sophia. He knew it was impossible to pretend.

Ten of Yesod's fateful twenty-four hours were spent in dreamless, disturbed sleep. When he awoke with a jolt the next morning he grabbed the clock off his bedside table and realized he was not guaranteed a place to sleep that night.

Quickly he dressed. Taking the picture from under his bed, Yesod covered it with an old blanket and tiptoed downstairs, hoping to leave the house unseen. He had decided to take the portrait to his bookstore for the time being and was relieved to find no one else in the house. Yesod started the engine of his old sedan. He didn't see or hear a sleek black sedan drive slowly past

his house, but at the bottom of the street the sleek Caddy turned and slowly came to a stop next to Yesod's car.

"*Meshugah!* Yesod!"

Yesod turned to see Gevurah's solemn face a few feet from his own. His suede-gloved hands were on the wheel, and he wore a new gray fedora that subtly emphasized his stylishly cut, graying hair.

"I want to talk with you, young man," said Gevurah as though he had been sent on an errand from the Almighty himself.

Yesod winced. He didn't want to see anyone, only to get his portrait away from disapproving eyes. Quickly he found the sunglasses he carried in his glove box and adjusted them over his nose. He glanced over his shoulder at the covered picture in the back seat. It couldn't be recognized. He was grateful for that.

"I'm in a hurry, Gevurah. Make it tomorrow or at *Shabbat*." He stopped cold. Should he go to *Shabbat*? Could he utter the *Shema*?

"No, now. Stay there, I'm parking. We'll talk."

Several minutes later, Gevurah had climbed into Yesod's front seat. Yesod mentioned his new hat.

"It's a gift from an old client," Gevurah chuckled. "For *Pesach*. I got him a divorce settlement that has the ex-wife paying *him*."

"Yesod looked at his watch. The clock of his mother's words was ticking away the little time he had left.

Gevurah was silent a moment, then gave Yesod a measuring look. "Your mother sent me, you know."

"My mother sent you? What did she send you to do? Kill me, maybe?"

"Your parents are very worried . . . and myself, as well."

So he knew, too. Yesod looked away. He guessed his mother had told the whole Jewish neighborhood that her son had a picture of Jesus Christ in her house.

"Go away, Gevurah," Yesod said. "Go see your rich client."

"Just tell me why, Yesod Chai. I want to know why."

"Why what?"

"Why you have a picture of this *Christian* in your house. Are you maybe selling it from your store? What?"

Yesod felt his temper rising. He looked into Gevurah's measuring eyes.

"I'm not selling it in the store. I found it, you understand? I wasn't looking. I just found it."

"Yesod, I'm your friend. You can tell me anything. You know that."

"Sure I can, and you'll report it to my parents. They already gave me an ultimatum! Is this a trial? Whose side are you on?"

"Sides, shmides. Whose side can I be on? Can you blame me? I know you so many years, and all of a sudden your grieving mother comes to my house in tears."

"In tears? My mother came to *you* in tears? *Gevult*. She shouldn't take this outside our house! I'm a grown man. I have rights. So what did she tell you?"

"Jews in the camps, they had rights, too. Taken away, just like that! She told me everything, Yesod. Everything you told her."

Yesod groaned. "Look, no one is right or wrong here. I've simply discovered something I want to learn more about. Why is my mother sending me a lawyer?"

Yesod started his engine, but Gevurah reached over and turned off the motor. The engine coughed, choked, and died. Yesod glared at this man he had known most of his adult life. They had shared innumerable *Shabbat* services side by side, held discussions into the morning hours on every talmudic and *Torah* principle, eaten, laughed, and worried together. But this was different, a question of ancient belief against the profound matter of a change in one's spirit. Yet it demanded, even in argument, a mutual respect. Yesod recalled their discussion earlier about Gevurah's cousin, Levi, and his secretive exodus to a church meeting of *goyim*. Was he, too, headed in that direction?

"Gevurah. Get out of my car. My time is evaporating. I'll have nowhere to sleep tonight."

"You're going to put the picture in your store?"

"I'm not sure, I may end up there myself. My mother is not a tolerant woman."

"She's afraid of the bomb you planted upstairs."

"And you're here to defuse it?"

"Yesod, how many mandatory commandments are given to a Jew?"

Yesod, taken off guard, turned in surprise. "What now, a Hebrew School lesson? Six hundred thirteen."

"The first command against idolatry?"

"So you think I'm serving idols?"

"Exodus 20:3, Yesod. It is forbidden to believe in the existence of any but one G-d. Deuteronomy 6:4. Acknowledge His unity. Deuteronomy 10:6, cleave unto Him! Leviticus 22:32, sanctify His name!"

Gevurah the lawyer stopped abruptly and was silent a minute. Then he stroked his gray beard and lifted a forefinger into the air.

"Do you recall your *bar mitzvah*, Yesod?" he asked in a teasing tone with a sidelong glance at the man hunched in misery behind the steering wheel.

"My *bar mitzvah* was a wonderful day, Gevurah, as was yours." Yesod's rising anger made his throat constrict as he replied.

"You wore the *tallit*,[62] remember? You kissed it first, then said your prayers wrapped in that holy shawl. The Sabbath comes tomorrow, and you, the Jesus lover, cannot put on his *tallit* to pray. And what about the night of *Kol Nidre*?[63] You will atone without the *tallit*?"

---

[62] Prayer shawl used by males at religious services
[63] "All the vows." Part of service of Yom Kippur, the Day of Atonement

"Gevurah, enough! Stop it!"

"How will you be buried, Yesod? Not in your *tallit!*" He fairly spit out this last sentence and turned away, perhaps toward some imaginary jury, looking into the mirror of their disapproving faces.

"Gevurah, why do you shame me? I don't violate the commandments. No place is empty of G-d. His presence is everywhere, the very gate to the Infinite! This man, *Jeshua*, he was a Jew like us. A prophet. He taught only love. Where is the harm?"

"The harm, my sick, deluded friend, is that he told everybody the Almighty One was his father. He took the place of G-d. 'Follow me,' he said, 'the Law is dead, I have fulfilled it. He claimed to be the immortal son of G-d. And how did he fulfill it? He was murdered. Even himself he couldn't save."

Yesod looked up from his hands against the steering wheel, shaking his head slowly in disgust. Then, with an expression of triumph that came from knowledge new and reassuring, he gave testimony to the man beside him. "Yes, he let himself be murdered, it is true, and it was our blind Sanhedrin who ordered his death. He came not to save his *mortal* life, but that *we* could live he *gave up* his life, as he promised. Who but the *Mashiach* could do that? He lives, Gevurah. I have seen him. I know that he lives!"

Gevurah drew back in shock. Silence was heavy between them. Then he began to debate this new information, as though it were a dangerous and deceptive ploy against four-odd thousand years of Judaic thought. The rain surrounding them grew heavier, pelting the windows and demanding attention, but the two men in the car were oblivious to the world. On and on they argued, until an hour had passed, and still there was no change in either's attitude.

"I saw him, the *Sheckinah, the Tsaddik*.[64] He's real. He spoke to me, Gevurah."

"Impossible. Even rabbis, revered sages of Israel, have not spoken of seeing the *Sheckinah*," Gevurah said in a hushed, accusing tone. "How can he come to you, a *nebbish*, a nobody? It isn't done. You were deceived. It was a *dybbuk* you saw!"

Yesod laughed derisively, remembering the confrontation with his *dybbuk* in the alleyway beside Ali's store. Suddenly he remembered an obscure passage from *Talmud* on the nature of evil. Did the Devil exult in blinding men from the truth? If so, his tool was false doctrine.

"Gevurah, I'm tired and I've wasted an hour in this steamy car with you. Please, get out now, and let me alone." Yesod dropped his head on the steering wheel and grimaced in pain.

"You will become a lost and lonely soul." Gevurah pontificated as if he were before a jury. "Adrift, at the mercy of the devil. You are a Jew, not a *meshugah* Christian. Instead of embracing your heritage, you will be no more than a homeless wanderer. In place of natural kinship with your family, your congregation, your synagogue, you will live outside your covenant, an outcast, a seeker after a false G-d." Gevurah paused to cough, then intoned,

---

[64] A holy man, righteous, with supernatural powers

"You make ashamed the Eternal One. I have been your friend, Yesod. But no longer. You are not my kind. I hold a funeral for you. I mourn for your soul."

With that, Gevurah left Yesod's car for his own and drove quickly away. Yesod slumped against the steering wheel and let the tears of sorrow come down his face. He cried a long time, listening to the rain and thunder slam against his car, as if every martyred Jew throughout history had been a listener in Gevurah's imaginary jury box. When the storm abated, Yesod got out of his car and stretched. He took the portrait from the rear seat with a long and trembling sigh and carried it back into his parents' house and up the stairs, where he set it carefully and in full view on his bed. He gave the frame a last pat of affection, looking with love at his *Mashiach*.

"Now, my friend, it is Yesod who learns about suffering."

He left the house again and drove to his store for the day's business.

SHENIE-ESREH

(Twelve)

Darkness had come to claim the daylight as Yesod drove home after closing his store. He loved the misty curtain of blue that tinted the whitewashed homes along the streets near his home. Yellow porch lights lined the residential streets like mute stanchions along the new path of life that had opened to him only days before. He was acutely aware that his sense of self had changed, as if pure knowledge had been transplanted from an otherworldly source into his brain and heart. But Yesod was finding out that his heightened discernment had been bought at a horrendous price. He had made himself a stranger on familiar ground.

The synagogue, spiritual focus of a religious Jew, was the very root of his life. From its persistent, fertile stalk sprouted a love for his religion, linking him intrinsically to it like petals on a rose; *Torah*, *Shabbat*, the festivals, Hebrew and *Talmud* study, holidays

and *seders*, his family, friends, his lovely Sofia Tiferet. His territorial imperative was to lead a Jewish way of life, a perennial culture of a people turned determinedly backward. Until a few weeks earlier, Yesod Chai Eleazer could never have imagined it differently.

But in the wake of his visitation by the *Sheckinah* came unfamiliar companions. Yesod's senses were shifting, old boundaries falling away like earth disappearing beneath him in the upheaval of new against old, thrusting him into the quake's very epicenter. Loneliness dogged him. What he'd experienced set him suddenly apart. He felt marooned from the leisurely Jewish sociality he had always taken for granted. He had daily enjoyed a familiar neighborhood and a supportive family, but now his encounters brought only judgment, anger, and rejection. Perhaps never again would he have a place at his mother's table. He was in danger of becoming homeless, the synagogue was off limits or would be when Rabbi Schechter found him out, his betrothed had abandoned him, and his lifelong friend had pronounced him dead without hope of redemption.

Yet, for all his pain and his dissembling life, Yesod felt a new and urgent energy prick away at the black melancholy of his spirit, moving him forward, almost against his will. A new name was writing itself on his heavy heart. Old habits, ancient beliefs, unquestioned in his family throughout millennia, demanded examination. As he walked into his mother's house that evening, he realized that more than anything in his daily life, it was the mysteries of *Talmud* and *Kabbalah* that had been in his way. They were a veil of confusion obscuring the simple truth so recently presented to him with a clarity and impact impossible to ignore: *Jeshua is the Mashiach. He lives!* This *Jeshua*, restorer of the throne of David in fulfillment of all prophecy, the crucified, the risen Son, the living G-d of Israel, this humble shepherd who gave all he had to save mankind from death and sin, came in answer to a prayer. Yesod the Jew, deep in a pasture of mystic uncertainty waited to be rescued.

He ascended the stairs to his room. It took a moment before the sounds of ripping and his mother's mutterings accosted his ears on the landing. Fear suddenly grabbed him. He turned the corner in time to see flakes of canvas and paint flying across the carpet like leaves fleeing the tree in fall. His beloved portrait was strangling in Binah's angry hands. On his bed lay the painting, split through the center, its pane of glass askew on top.

Yesod screamed in terror. Binah held a steak knife to the print, and with sharp wicked slices to the face and body of the *Mashiach*, she attacked it mercilessly.

"*Mamale*, stop, stop! My picture! Please! Oh my G-d, no!"

He rushed to her, grabbing the knife away, but the painting was already destroyed. He pushed her to the bed. Binah screamed in anger. The heavyset woman warned him.

"Let go, Yesod. I told you. Get it out of here!"

Mother and son wrestled together, their voices splitting the air.

"What are you doing to me? How can you destroy it? You, my mother!"

Binah fell to the floor, and Yesod held her down while he threw the steak knife across his room into a pile of books. But she tore out of his grip and pushed him off balance. She struggled to her feet, breathing heavily, for she was no longer young or fit. He lay before her, too amazed to move.

"I warned you. I told you. Twenty-four hours. Now I come up here and find it sitting on your bed like a prize possession?"

"This is my room. You have no right!" Yesod struggled to his feet, tears suffocating him.

Binah saw a fragment of the picture laying before her and quickly bent down to swoop it up.

"This," she said, waving it before her son's contorted face. "This is what gives me the right. How can you betray your grandparents, your heritage? How many of our family died in camps? You saw pictures! How many came back to Israel from Germany and Russia, to be free from *goyim*, free to be Jews, to worship as Jews! Obligation! Duty! Chai Eleazer, you're one of the *chosen*, yet you betray your birthright! I'm your mother. I'm saving you from yourself."

Yesod's heart threatened to burst through his chest. "*Mamale*," he shouted, pointing to the picture laying dismembered on the rug, "this man is not the cause or the problem. He came to save us, to show us there's more—"

Binah screamed and covered her ears. "No! No more, no more! You have lost your reason, Yesod! Ask forgiveness! The first night of *Pesach*. You are like leaven. No longer is this your house!

No son of mine is a Christian. Do you hear? I did not raise a *goy*. Get out! Get out, and take this miserable picture with you!"

Binah sobbed in great heaves. Yesod stared at his mother in shock as she ordered him out of the house forever. Then, stomping past the pieces of faux canvas paper littering the old carpet, she ran from the room in tears.

SHALOSH-ESREH

(Thirteen)

In the wake of his mother's words, Yesod prostrated himself on the bed. He fought his anger, knowing she was incapable of seeing things differently. He understood her grief and wanted to tell her of his love and respect for her lifelong help and protective influence. But he knew, too, that her logic was undeniable. Untold generations of faithful Jews had accepted starvation, death, and disfigurement, rather than accept Christianity or paganism. Jewish history was woven from centuries of worldwide rebellion, murder, suicide, refusal by masses of Jews to compromise a single point of their religious or cultural belief! How many millions went to their noble end with the *Shema* etched in their hearts and borne upon their lips while in the throes of death? They died knowing they were the Chosen Ones, followers of Moses in a land Moses never knew. It was Yesod's heritage, his legacy. His portion of that

burden could not be compromised without severe reprisals from his family.

Finally, he sat up and surveyed his room. The portrait lay in segments on the carpet. Binah had sliced it through the middle first, then downward, severing the tree trunk from the figure of Jesus. That portion lay curled near the bedroom door, while the upper section was torn into smaller pieces without aid of the knife, for Binah in her fury wanted to wreak her havoc quickly, to banish the evil she imagined, to protect her only child. These ragged pieces of canvas were scattered nearer his bed. *That's me down there*, he thought. *Murdered, destroyed, a life ripped apart*.

Now Yesod recalled the *dybbuk*'s ominous prophecy of suicide: "*By yer own hand!*" Suddenly he understood. It had been a pronouncement not of impending physical death but of spiritual rebirth, a change he would choose to make, *want* to make. *I must die as a Jew before I can be restored in Christ.*

Yesod moved to the floor and slowly picked up each piece, wondering at its oily sheen and underlying stiffness, resembling dried old blood. He found a plate and piled it with small and crusty bits of canvas, like crumbs of bread, touching each to his lips as he did so, in a kind of sacramental kiss. It gave him new determination. *These are like the separate parts of a man, each with its own purpose but relying on each other for a fullness of unity, as Kabbalah teaches*.

Yesod felt an overwhelming compassion for the man in the portrait, and this gave him strength to go on. He wondered how he would find another picture like this so he could look again

upon the sweet, strong face of his *Mashiach*. But as he moved around his room, silently gathering the leaves of his vandalized portrait, a thought came to him. Quickly, he began to lay the segments out again like a bizarre puzzle. One large piece that had been the praying hands had scribbling on the back of it, hidden from sight by the frame's backboard. Yesod guessed it to be a scripture from the New Testament a former owner must have scrawled on it long ago.

> *Wherefore the law was our schoolmaster to bring us unto Christ that we might be justified by faith. For ye are all the children of G-d by faith in Christ Jesus. And if ye be Christ's, then are ye Abraham's seed, and heirs according to the promise.* [Galatians 3:24, 26, 29]

Seeing these words for the first time, Yesod stared at them in amazement. *Yes*, he thought, *I am Yeshua's and I am of the seed of the prophets*. His heart lifted as he read, the joy of understanding spreading through him. Within a short time Yesod had pieced together the overhanging tree and the head and body of Jesus. He gazed at the cracked and patched arrangement and tears welled up in his eyes as he recognized the face of his Savior. He worked with urgency until the whole canvas lay in one disfigured, but reassembled, mass on the carpet. As a final touch, glass and broken frame were lovingly placed on top and it was again oddly, eerily, whole at his feet.

Standing over the portrait Yesod looked into it. He thought for a moment that he discerned his own thin reflection in the glass and smiled. He remained there until he had memorized every

detail of the picture. Then he went to his closet, removed his several valises and began to pack his things. Downstairs, his uncle and aunt had arrived, greeted loudly by his parents. It was the first night of *Pesach* and time to begin the *Seder* meal.

No one looked at Yesod as he descended the stairs, carrying just his three bags, two of them bulging with his books. With the air of a man attending to important business he let himself out the front door and carried the bags to his car.

"Where are you going, Yesod Chai?"

The voice was Sofia's, lilting and even, like the soft night wind that blew past his ears. Yesod turned in surprise to find her almost at his side. Her black hair was held at her neck with a red scarf that set off glistening ruby red earrings he didn't remember seeing before. She wore an expression of sweet kindness, guileless and innocent, as when they had first begun to court. Tonight he noticed the darkness beneath her eyes and the new, taut lines at her mouth. She had suffered, too, without him. He tried to remember how her lips tasted in that moment, to feel the old love for her, but somehow he could not.

"Sofia Tiferet, how surprising to see you here. I'm just leaving for my store now, to arrange some things."

He loaded the bags into his back seat and slammed the door shut. He knew she was studying him, looking for a vulnerable glance or smile. He would not grant her that. Was she here to reconcile, to make amends? Had her father sent her to work things

out? A picture of the ruined, reassembled portrait on the rug upstairs came to mind like a mirror.

"Yesod, I . . . we should . . . I mean, I want to talk this over, Yesod, a *bissel*." She faked a small laugh and stopped, waiting for him, unsure of her ground.

"I thought we did that," Yesod answered, looking away from her. He felt dead, as though he'd swallowed a potion that turned off all feeling. "Your feelings were clear, Sofia. What more is there to say?"

She smiled gently, sensing he still loved her beneath his hurt expression.

"Perhaps I was too harsh the other day," she began. "Jumping to conclusions. You meant only to tell me your impressions of the moment. I reacted so quickly that I—"

Yesod turned to her. His feeling was that she had grown thinner since their last meeting. Wafts of her hair lifted in the light breeze, and the faintly cinnamon fragrance she wore returned his mind to happier times together. She looked angelic, complete. Yes, there was no question he loved her as he would no other in years to come, but her words sobered him.

"They were not impressions of the moment, Sofia Tiferet, but conclusions I have reached, knowledge that is undeniable." He waited, looking into her face to see if her anger would return, but her black eyes merely regarded him. She might have been a portrait. Had she really changed her mind? He looked at her harder, trying to see in her eyes that same hatred that had con-

torted her picture perfect features into those of a hag (or a *dybbuk*?), but there was only sweetness.

"I see. I was hoping. . ." She hesitated, hugging herself against a sudden chill. Her expression was suddenly downcast.

The breezes increased in strength, carrying their past away like old leaves losing their color. Yesod waited, for a moment unsure of their politics. Her father would have forbidden Sofia to see him again. She must have sneaked away.

She fumbled with her words. "Our fight, it was . . . I mean, we were not sure . . . I could tolerate . . . I mean, if you really love this . . . this . . . Oh, Yesod, I do love you!" Fervently she cried out for him. She reached out, desperate for her lover's embrace.

Filled suddenly with the same longing, he came to her. "Sofia, oh my love, my darling love." They swayed in the soft evening wind like two flowers entwined, mesmerized with hope.

It will be all right, he thought, *it will work itself out*. And his heart began to quiet. He felt them sigh together. Was any marriage perfect, did not problems bring lovers closer together? "Yesod?"

"Yes, my *shayna*?"

"Please don't be angry, my love . . . but surely we'll raise our children as Jews?"

Her words found their way into Yesod's pounding heart and stopped it cold. He would remember later that he felt himself freeze. It was not a question, but a soft mandate, an attempt to forgive him for his new madness. In the heat of romance, their

most important differences had been forgotten. But now . . .

He pulled back and looked into teary black eyes fresh with joy. His beloved. He knew his answer would be the severing sword. He forced the final words from his throat.

"No, Sofia Tiferet. No, we cannot raise them as Jews when there is a *Mashiach* already come. They must seek him, as I do, and I pray you will want that, too. Do you see that?"

Yesod heard her breath catch in a moan, and it came to him that it was this one question she had come to ask.

Sofia began to speak, then stopped. Her eyes shut. She looked away. The still night was listening. The wind sent messages of sorrow. They stood a while longer together, not wanting to move away from each other right away. But slowly Yesod withdrew and buttoned his coat around him. Sofia watched him in silence, her lips parted in a hesitant smile. She stepped back as he came around to her and offered his hand. She put her smaller one in his. Why, he wondered as he felt her warm flesh upon his palm, was so much of love a contest of faith that took divergent paths?

"I will always love you," she said with a sudden rush. "Oh, *Chaili*, must this be?" She began to cry softly, like a young thing alone in the dark, afraid. A gentle breeze brought the smell of her cinnamon hair.

He thought of the long journey he would take from her, their unborn babies he had already envisioned. He caressed her as she came to him and cried against his coat, cooing softly. Then, firmly,

he moved her away forever. He was anxious to be going, not to allow himself to weaken further.

"You will be fine," Yesod said to comfort her. "You'll raise many fine babies, you'll see." The thought that they would not be his babies stabbed at his heart.

"And you, what will happen to you? I fear for you, Yesod." Her hand came up to her throat and held it as if in pain.

Yesod said nothing, knowing he would sorrow forever because of the choice she had made for them. He recalled suddenly the *dybbuk*'s prophecy. Death now would be balm, he anguished.

"I am myself taking the journey we could have shared, Sofia. There is no going back for me now. My regret is that you chose as you did. But one day you will understand as I do, and your joy then will be full."

She looked at him in puzzlement. Yesod felt the long suppressed tears begin to drench his eyes. "I love you, Sofia Tiferet, my *shayna*," Yesod told her, his voice breaking. The dam of sorrow broke then, and he hurriedly got into his car before she could reply.

As he pulled away he saw Sofia in his rear view mirror, huddled over, still clutching her throat as if frozen in a question mark. Turning the corner a final time, he threw a glance backward at his parents' home, then headed for his store where he would live for a time. He brushed away tears, trying to control his racking sobs. Gevurah and Hesed would dedicate the first night of *Pesach*

without his presence in perhaps fifteen years, and for the first time in his life he was self-excluded from a *seder*.

It was nearing midnight, the moon was only a sliver but it wore a halo of light. The shopping district lay before him. No one was on the streets as he pulled his car around to the parking lot behind his store. The grief he felt were not only for his loss but extended to all those he loved and to a hundred generations of his people who were blind to the great saving truths he had discovered.

But as Yesod consoled his heart and contemplated his future, a new excitement began to grow in him, gently replacing his grief. He remembered then the embossed copy of the New Testament Ali had shown him and hungered for it and the mysteries he would come upon in its pages.

Silently a prayer came into his heart, unlike any he'd uttered in his life. *Dearest Savior, wait for me, I come to thee with a wondering heart.*

When he unpacked his bags later that night and sorted out his things, he took his *Kabbalah* from its protective cover, and after letting it lay lovingly in his hands a while, he put it squarely in the Bargain Bin with a hastily scrawled note that said:

Very well used. Great for starters. ***FREE!***

Glossary of Hebrew and Yiddish Terms

Alta cocker — Old fool. (Yiddish)

Amayn (ah may n) — Hebrew pronunciation of "Amen."

Ashkenazim (Ash′ ke naz′ im) — The Germanic people. A German Jew. Also a name applied to Jews of Central and Eastern Europe.

Bar Mitzvah (Bar Mitz′vah) — "Son of the commandment." When a 13-year old Jewish boy symbolically becomes a man, responsible for his actions and faith. Held as a confirmation ceremony.

Bet midrash (bet mid′ rash) — House of study.

Bet din (bet′ din) — House of judgement.

Bet tefilah (bet tef′ eel′ ah) — House of prayer.

Bissel (bissel) — A little bit. (Yiddish)

B'nai Brith (b'nay' brit) — Children of the Covenant. A national women's Jewish philanthropic organization.

Bris from "*brit*" — meaning covenant. Ashkenazic word. A circumcision ceremony for male infants at 8 days of life. Symbolic of the persistence of Israel and called seriously the "Seal of G-d."

Chanukah (Chan' nu' kah) — Feast of Dedication. Celebrates the victory of the Maccabees over the Syrians in 167 B.C.E. in their fight for religious freedom. Begins on 25th day of Jewish lunar month of Kislev (December). See John 10:22–23.

Daven (da' ven) — To pray. A Jew sometimes faces East toward Israel when *davening*. A constant forward and backward movement from the knee by the Jewish person praying usually accompanies the prayer.

Dybbuk (dyb' buk) — Evil spirit, demon; enters the soul of a person; a migrating spirit looking for a body to inhabit. (Yiddish)

Elohim — One of the names of G-d.

Faftik! (faf' tik) — Enough! We're finished! (Yiddish)

Galut (gal' ut) — Alienated, the exiled. (Yiddish)

Gelt — Cash (Yiddish)

Gevalt! (ge' valt) — Fear, astonishment, cry for help. (Yiddish)

G-d (God) — Mention of the Almighty's name in print is done in a manner that will not offend Him. This is one of His holy names.

*Goyim (*goy′ im) — A non-Jew, a gentile. (Yiddish)

Hak a chainik (hoc′ a′ chyn′ ik*)* — Talk nonsense. (Yiddish)

Halakhah (hal′ a′ chah) — The code of behavior represented by the Law of Moses in *Torah* and *Talmud* writings. Codified and clarified teachings of centuries.

Hasid (ha′ sid) — Pious one. A disciple of the great rabbi, called *Baal Shem Tov* (Master of the Good Name) (Name of God), who in an eighteenth century movement in Judaism emphasized simple faith, joy in worship, enjoying everyday pleasures. Also means a mystic, one who is anticlerical.

Hazzan (haz′ zan) — The cantor (singer), a paid professional singer who assists the *rabbi* in the services. The *hazzan* can perform the *rabbi*'s tasks in his absence.

Herem (her′ em) — A turncoat. (Yiddish)

Huppah (hup′ ah) — The wedding canopy. A couple is considered to be the king and queen of the day. Posts are held aloft by family members. A rite of passage.

Kabbalah (ka′ bal′ ah) — That which has been received. The body of Jewish mystical and esoteric tradition that can be received by faithful searchers. Its principles have influenced all of modern Judaic thought. Cabalism was a pre-Middle Ages

attempt to fathom the mysteries of G-d. Supernatural in content, *Kabbalah* is a compilation of arcane formulas that help mankind apprehend G-d's presence. Assumes the coming of the Messiah in latter days. Several of the names of characters in *People of the Book* correspond to ancient names for the lights and powers (characteristics) of G-d: the ten *Sefirot* (sef e **rōt**):

The *Kabbalah* "tree": Italicized names are those given to characters in this book.

Keter:	The pure, ungraspable crown of G-d.
Binah:	Understanding, symbol of nurture.
Cochmah:	Wisdom, beginning of all things.
Gevurah:	Power, judgment.
Hesed:	Love, grace.
Tiferet:	Beauty, harmony.
Hod:	Splendor, prophecy.
Netsah:	Eternity.
Yesod:	Procreative life force of universe.
Malchut, Sheckinah:	Presence, Kingdom, communion of Israel.

Kibbitz (ki′ bitz) — Talker; to josh, tease, flatter, butt in. (Yiddish)

Kiddush (kid′ ush) — Prayer and ceremony sanctifying Jewish Sabbath and holy days. Genesis 2:1–3 is recited and a cup of wine is drunk.

Kineahora (kin′ a′ hora) — A magic phrase that wards off evil. (Yiddish)

Kol Nidre — "All the vows" ritualistic prayers. Part of service of Yom Kippur, Day of Atonement, last of the 10 "Days of Awe" following the Jewish New Year, Rosh Hashonah.

Kosher (kosh′ er) — Means appropriate, ritually clean in accordance with Old Testament dietary laws, food fit for humans to eat. Believed to strengthen a Jew's dedication as one of G-d's instruments to bring redemption to the world.

Maccabees (Mac-a-bees) — Family of Jewish patriots who led successful revolt against Syrians (175-164 B.C.E.) and ruled Palestine until 37 B.C.E.)

Madele (may′ de′ la) — A young Jewish girl. (Yiddish)

Malach — A holy angel. Literally in Hebrew, a king's messenger.

Malkhut — Refers to the kingdom of G-d. One of the titles used to avoid using the actual name of the Father, *melek* in Hebrew.

Mashiach (ma′ shee′ ach) — Messiah, anointed one. To Christians, Jesus Christ. To Jews the word has several meanings: a deliverer, a David, a peaceful Israel, a mortal or immortal Savior. Messianic Jews know Jesus the Christ as the world's *Maschiach*.

Matzoh (ma′tzoh) — Unleavened bread, usually in cracker form.

Mazeltov (ma' zel' tov) Congratulations, good luck.

Menorah — Candelabrum. The Sabbath menorah has seven branches and an eighth (*shammes*-servant) lights the seven. The Passover candelabrum has eight branches and a *shammes*.

Mensch (men' sh) — A gentleman, prosperous, propertied. (Yiddish)

Meshugah (me' shu'gah) — Crazy, wild, absurd. (Yiddish)

Mezzuzah (me' zu'zah) — Small oblong container put on the right front door jamb of a home, kissed by the occupants as they enter and leave. Contains scroll fragment from Deuteronomy 6:4–9, 11:13–21. The mezuzah consecrates the home.

Minyan (min' yan) — A quorum. Ten men required to begin a religious service. Originally, of Levites. Now, few Jews know their tribe.

Nebbish — An unfortunate person, one to be pitied. (Yiddish)

Ner Tamid (nare' ta' mid) — In Jewish theology, the "Everlasting Light." After the Maccabees took their temple back from the Syrians in 167 B.C.E. they found a cruse of olive oil which was almost depleted. It burned for eight days, a miracle commemorated in *Chanukah*.

Pale — Pale of Settlement. A territory or district named and occupied by Jews who were banished there between 1215 –1870. The 386,000 square mile area between the Baltic and

the Black Sea which included the Ukraine, Byelorussia, Lithuania and much of Poland.

Pesach — Passover. Begins 15th day of the Jewish month of Nissan (March), lasts eight days outside of Israel. The first of three major festivals with historical and agricultural significance. Beginning of the harvest season in Israel. Probably the most significant observance related to Pesach involves the removal of *chametz* (leaven) from our homes. This commemorates the Jews leaving Egypt in a hurry without time to let their bread rise. Also symbolic of removing the arrogance from our souls. Primary observances of Pesach are related to the Exodus from Egypt after generations of slavery. See Exodus 1–15.

Rabbi (ra′ bye) — Also *rebbe*. Jewish teacher of Torah and Talmud, one who can be ordained by other rabbis, usually by his seminary. Not an intermediary between G-d and the congregation but chosen for character, leadership, learning. The spiritual leader of a synagogue. Functions are similar to a clergyman. A Chasidic rabbi can inherit the position or be invited to the position.

Schleimeil (shle méal) — Foolish person, unlucky, unfortunate, clumsy, social misfit. (Yiddish)

Schlepped (shlep′ ed) — Carried, dragged along. (Yiddish)

Schul — Synagogue.

Sephardim (Sef' ar deem) — Spanish and Portuguese Jews and their descendants. In recent times the designation applies to Moroccan Jews, also.

Shabbat (Sha' bat) — Sabbath. Refers to Sabbath and those synagogue services, celebrated every Friday at sundown through Saturday at sundown.

Shayna (shay' na) — Beautiful in character, spirit.

Sheckinah (shek' in' ah) — G-d's spirit, His essence, His dwelling place, the holy spirit of *Adonai*, G-d.

Shema (she ma') — Or *Shema Yisroel*. The Jewish creedal prayer. "Hear, O Israel, the lord our G-d, the lord is One." [Deuteronomy 6:4–9] Proclaims basic unity of Jewish belief in monotheism. In Judaism no Mashiach is yet recognized nor is there a defined Holy Spirit. The final word "one" refers lexically in Hebrew to both singular and plural deities.

Sholom (sho' lom) — Peace. A greeting, salutation, blessing.

Shtetl (shtet'l) — Jewish communities, villages of East Europe during WWII where the culture of the Ashkenazim flourished in confined surroundings.

Siddur (sid' ur) — The Jews' prayer and song book for all holidays and special observations including *Shabbat* services. Revised periodically, it reflects the religious ceremonies of Jewish people in an evolving culture.

Tallit — A replica lambskin garment worn by Jewish men, referred to as a prayer shawl.

Talmud (tal′ mud) — Means student/scholar in Hebrew. Sixty-three books which feature interpretations of the *Torah* in commentary, dialogues, debates, and conclusions. These tractates speak to ethics, spirituality, regulations, legal outcomes of a Jewish nation in *Diaspora* (dispersion).

Torah (To′ rah) — The first five books of the Bible, called variously the Pentateuch, the written *Torah* (scrolls), and the Law of Moses. They are Genesis, Exodus, Leviticus, Numbers, and Deuteronomy. *Torah* can also refer to all the religious writings (the Old Testament to Christians) which includes the writings of the Prophets and the other sacred writings; *Hagiographa*.

Tsaddik (tza′ dik) — A righteous or holy man, often with supernatural powers.

Tsetsele (tzet′ ze′ leh) — Term of endearment between lovers and the betrothed. (Could be Yiddish)

Vay is mere (vay′ is′ mere) — Oh, dear me! (Yiddish)

Vunderlech — Wonderful. (German)

Yarmulke (Ashkenazic) (yom′ ul′ ka) — The Hebrew word is *kippah*. Skullcap worn by Jewish males who observe the Law of Moses.

Yeshua or Jeshua — General meaning: salvation. An Aramaic word meaning "he is saved." The Hebrew proper name for Jesus of Nazareth, by which he was called.

Hebrew equivalent for Greek name of Jesus (Iaesous) from Greek New Testament in Acts 7:45, Heb 4:8. Also defined as: "free," "deliverance" and "victory" over death. Thus, Jesus is a savior, deliverer and redeemer.

Alternately this word is represented as Yehoshua or Yeshu with either (Y) or (J) as the first letter, but with a "Y" pronunciation. In the Old Covenant (Old Testament), Numbers 13:8, Joshua (Hoshea), is the central figure. Moses evidently changed it to Yehoshua.

Yiddish — A language derived from medieval High German, spoken by East European Jews and other countries. Written in Hebrew alphabet with heavy German contribution of words as well as Russian, Polish, English, some remnants of Old Italian and Old French. Earliest records of Yiddish from 1000 A.D. to about 1750 and forward are documented in old texts. Initially, Yiddish arose in the ghettos, but in modern life it is fast fading from usage among youngest Jews.

Yom Kippur (yom′ ki′ pur) — The Day of Atonement. A solemn yearly Jewish holiday given over to repentance and cleansing of the soul. Last of the annual ten days of repentance, fasting, and confession of sins. Occurs at sundown on the 9th day of Tishri (September) of Jewish lunar calendar.

Zayde — Grandfather. (Yiddish)

About the Author

Marlena Tanya Muchnick was baptized a member of the Church of Jesus Christ of Latter-day Saints on April 6, 1988 after years of searching to know God's purpose for her. Her personal story is told in *Notes of A Jewish Convert to the LDS Church: Conversion of a* Soul . . . Marlena, a returned senior missionary, is a popular speaker who considers her books, songs and uplifting, informative firesides on the Jewish way of life to be a part of her continuing mission to help teach the Jewish people that Jesus (Yeshua) is the savior of the world. She invites her readers to correspond and to visit her websites, *www.jewishconvert-lds.com* and *www.peopleofthebookk-judaica.com* for updates.

This is Marlena's fourth published work. She hopes to produce it as a play. She is currently working on a novel about the Jewish holocaust experience in the Ukraine.

Marlena serves as gospel doctrine teacher in her ward. She and her husband, Daniel Baker, plan to serve a mission in the near future.

NOW AVAILABLE FROM THE AUTHOR

Notes of A Jewish Convert to the LDS Church: Conversion of a Soul
Softbound. Marlena's conversion from Judaism. Riveting story!
Useful glossary of terms and appendices included.

Life Changing Testimonies of the Lord Jesus Christ
Softbound. Four chapters on life, Jewishness of Jesus
PLUS 13 fascinating stories of conversion and progression.

Adventures With The Angels of Love
Softbound fiction. Errant boy is taught true Gospel
by angels through dreams. A mystery for the young in spirit.

Song of the Christ: A Spoken Psalm and Into His Rest. Two Songs
Sheet Music. Latter-day psalms, appropriate for church.
By Gabriele Burgess and Marlena Tanya Muchnick

Marlena's Conversion Story: A fireside talk with original songs
Recorded in Seattle 11/01. Helps with conversion.
Audio Cassette –75 minutes

Marlena reads People of the Book
Her newest fiction novel in her inimitable style!
2 – 100-minute audio tape cassettes or 4 CD pack

To PLACE ORDER, obtain more information on products, study ***The Seven Feasts Of Israel***, enjoy ***Songs In The Spirit*** **SCHEDULE A FIRESIDE** and much more:

Visit Marlena's website *www.jewishconvert-lds.com*

INTERESTED IN KNOWING *EVEN MORE* ABOUT JUDAISM?
Also visit Marlena's informational linking website:
peopleofthebook-judaica.com